PERIODIC CORRELATIONS

THE PHYSICAL INORGANIC CHEMISTRY SERIES

Robert A. Plane and Michell J. Sienko, Editors

Oxygen: Elementary Forms and Hydrogen Peroxide — *M. Ardon (Hebrew University of Jerusalem)*

Inorganic Reaction Mechanisms — *J. O. Edwards (Brown)*

Metal Ions in Aqueous Solution — *J. P. Hunt (Washington State)*

Inorganic Chemistry of Nitrogen — *W. L. Jolly (Berkeley)*

The Solid-State Chemistry of Binary Metal Hydrides — *G. G. Libowitz (Kennecott Copper)*

Boron Hydrides — *W. N. Lipscomb (Harvard)*

Elements of Inorganic Chemistry — *R. A. Plane and R. E. Hester (Cornell)*

Periodic Correlations — *R. L. Rich (Bethel College)*

Physical Inorganic Chemistry — *M. J. Sienko and R. A. Plane (Cornell)*

PERIODIC CORRELATIONS

RONALD RICH

Bethel College

W. A. BENJAMIN, INC.

1965   New York   Amsterdam

PERIODIC CORRELATIONS

Library of Congress Catalog Card Number 65–10941
Manufactured in the United States of America

*The manuscript was put into production on June 11, 1964;
this volume was published on March 15, 1965*

W. A. BENJAMIN, INC.
New York, New York 10016

Editors' Foreword

In recent years few fields of chemistry have expanded at a rate to match that of inorganic chemistry. Aside from the stimulus afforded by the demand for new materials, a primary cause for the resurgence has been the application of physics and physical chemistry concepts to inorganic problems. As a result, both researchers active in the field and students entering the field need to become as thoroughly familiar with physical concepts as with descriptive information. However, there is presently no single point of view sufficiently general to organize the entire discipline. Instead, various points of view have arisen corresponding to the most powerful methods of attack in each research area. The synthesis of these different points of view constitutes the present series of monographs. Each monograph is contributed by an inorganic chemist active in a particular research area and reflects the methods of approach characteristic to that area. The operational procedure has been to invite able scientists to write where their interests lead them.

The series fulfills several functions. Through flexible selection of several of the monographs to supplement the introductory volume, it can be used as a textbook for an advanced inorganic chemistry course that makes full use of physical chemistry prerequisites. As a series in total, it is a reference treatise of inorganic chemistry systematized by

v

physical principles. Finally, each monograph by itself represents a specialist's introduction to a specific research field.

It is hoped that the authors contributing to this series have succeeded in directing attention to unsolved problems and that their efforts will be repaid by continued research advances in inorganic chemistry.

M. J. SIENKO
R. A. PLANE

Ithaca, New York
February 1963

Preface

One of the fascinations of inorganic chemistry is the existence of a wide variety of relationships among the elements and their properties—relationships that show an encouraging degree of order, but a tantalizing variability and novelty. These qualities make the "family of elements" an apt metaphor: while members of a family have much in common, each member also has his own individual personality. The quality of relatedness among elements makes periodic tables possible. But the diversity of their interrelationships bars any one table from a monopoly on the advantages. For this reason, and in order to broaden the reader's acquaintance, a variety of forms (see Reference 1 at the end of this Preface) will be used throughout this book. (The arrangements of Tables 4–5 or 6–1, however, can be assumed to be the background for discussion when no other is specified.)

The central purpose of this book is to present some of the important patterns in similarities and differences among the chemistries of all the elements, together with (hopefully) reasonable but sometimes speculative explanations for these patterns and with indications of outstanding gaps in our knowledge of fact or theory. Textbook space is usually available only for exposition of the meaning of a concept or property, such as oxidation state, with a few examples and subsequent application to particular cases, but not for discovery of its periodicity or the related web of cause and effect.

Where periodicity *has* been examined, either it has (sometimes) meant simply describing successive groups of elements or compounds without much attention to the reasons for the trends, or physical rather than chemical properties have been emphasized. The present treatment does not avoid all discussion of smaller topics or groups of substances or, especially, of significant physical properties; the emphasis, however, is on integration and the ability to predict or at least to rationalize trends in chemical reactivity. I hope this approach will prove stimulating to students and practicing chemists, and that it will make the otherwise unwieldy mass of descriptive chemistry much more fun to learn.

After several chapters on electronic, structural, and other fundamental properties, the second half of the book gives attention to test-tube chemistry and is based largely on the understandings partially developed earlier. The writing, as only part of a series for one course, is necessarily condensed; for this reason, both the use of the references and the thoughtful consideration of additional illustrative examples not given here are especially important. It has not been possible either to discuss all the arguments for and against the various interpretations of chemical phenomena or always to point out the many uncertainties in the "facts" described.

References are chosen with some emphasis on relatively recent reviews and general discussions. Some especially useful and perhaps less-known sources of numerical data on aqueous chemistry not found conveniently or at all in the usual encyclopedias are listed at the end of Chapter 5 (to minimize repetition) for the entire second half of the book. References on complexes of transition elements with unsaturated ligands are given at the end of Chapter 1 and not repeated. Periodicity in other organometallics is well taken care of elsewhere (Reference 2). Books that appear regularly in series are handled partly like journals, for both conciseness and consistency Some references are not specifically cited in the text.

A few terms and symbols have been modified from American practice in the direction of the I.U.P.A.C. recommendations (Reference 3).

Thanks are extended to Drs. Alan Davison, Martin Gouterman, and E. G. Rochow for reading and commenting on various parts of the manuscript and to Professor Rochow for his hospitality during and beyond this work. The Linda Hall Library in Kansas City provided nearly all the references not available at Harvard. Finally, I am indebted to my students for some of the questions explored here.

References

1. E. G. Mazurs, *Types of Graphic Representation of the Periodic System of Chemical Elements* (La Grange, Illinois: Edward G. Mazurs, 1957). Also, *J. Chem. Ed.,* 1964, Vol. 41: R. T. Sanderson, p. 187; T. Ternstrom, p. 190; H. K. Griff, p. 191 (new periodic tables).

2. E. G. Rochow, D. T. Hurd, and R. N. Lewis, *The Chemistry of Organometallic Compounds* (New York: John Wiley, 1957), Chapter 1, "General Considerations," largely periodicity and underlying factors.

3. J. A. Christiansen, "Manual of Physico-Chemical Symbols and Terminology," *J. Am. Chem. Soc.,* 1960, **82,** 5517, and "Nomenclature of Inorganic Chemistry," *op. cit.,* p. 5523.

RONALD RICH

North Newton, Kansas
June 1964

Contents

PERIODIC CORRELATIONS

1

Electron Configuration

1-1 CLASSIFICATION OF ELEMENTS BY ELECTRON CONFIGURATION

Now that the basis of chemical properties in electronic structure is recognized, periodic tables can be based on this structure. Nevertheless, the correlation of properties with electron configuration is not simple. Thus, helium is certainly a noble gas chemically, but its spectrum and electron configuration are those of an alkaline-earth element. That is, it has no outer p electrons while all the other noble gases, but none of the alkaline-earth elements, have a complete outer p subshell. (We could, of course, define alkaline-earth elements as those with two s electrons and six p *vacancies* in the outer shell. The noble gases would then be those without any s or p vacancies in the outer shell.) Furthermore, electronic structures themselves are fairly complicated. This precludes any reasonably simple periodic chart based exactly on these structures and is one reason for the use of various forms of the chart in this book and elsewhere.

Table 1–1 shows the assignments[1a,e] of some of the outer groups of electrons to the various shells and subshells in isolated atoms in the ground state. These assignments, which are somewhat uncertain, especially where the f subshells are incomplete, show the basis for the main features of chemical periodicity. It is important to realize, however, that most chemical properties depend very much on the electron configurations in ionized and excited states and in molecules, as well as on the availabilities or energies of the various filled and unfilled orbitals in these species. We are fortunate, then, that the practice of classifying elements by the configurations in the ground states of neutral isolated atoms is not completely misleading.

Because of the many irregularities, discussed in the next section, it will be convenient to use simplified assignments of

Table 1-1 *Electron Configurations in Atoms*

														Sc	Ti
														$4s^2$	$4s^2$
														$3d^1$	$3d^2$
														Y	Zr
														$5s^2$	$5s^2$
														$4d^1$	$4d^2$
La	Ce	Pr	Nd	Pm	Sm	Eu	Gd	Tb	Dy	Ho	Er	Tm	Yb	Lu	Hf
$6s^2$	$6s^2$	$6s^2$	$6s^2$	$6s^2$	$6s^2$	$6s^2$	$6s^2$	$6s^2$	$6s^2$	$6s^2$	$6s^2$	$6s^2$	$6s^2$	$6s^2$	$6s^2$
$5d^1$	$5d^1$						$5d^1$							$5d^1$	$5d^2$
	$4f^1$	$4f^3$	$4f^4$	$4f^5$	$4f^6$	$4f^7$	$4f^7$	$4f^9$	$4f^{10}$	$4f^{11}$	$4f^{12}$	$4f^{13}$	$4f^{14}$	$4f^{14}$	$4f^{14}$

Ac	Th	Pa	U	Np	Pu	Am	Cm	Bk	Cf	Es	Fm	Md	No	Lw
$7s^2$	$7s^2$	$7s^2$	$7s^2$	$7s^2$	$7s^2$	$7s^2$	$7s^2$							
$6d^1$	$6d^2$	$6d^1$	$6d^1$	$6d^1$			$6d^1$							
		$5f^2$	$5f^3$	$5f^4$	$5f^6$	$5f^7$	$5f^7$							

quantum numbers for classification and discussion. Table 1–2 presents the designations to be used hereafter. Under each chemical symbol the first number and letter denote the subshell considered as becoming filled in that part of the table. Immediately following is the number of electrons assigned to this subshell for the atom in question. Since this sometimes differs from the actual configuration, the final number is not written as a superscript and is to be taken primarily as a group number. Above the chemical symbol is the atomic number, included because Table 1–2, unlike Table 1–1, has some breaks in the natural order of atomic numbers.

We can now speak of, for example, "group **p3**," "row **2**" (or "row **2sp**"), "column **f9**," or "row **5d**." We should remember that the number of valence electrons theoretically available to

	H	He
	$1s^1$	$1s^2$

	Li	Be
	$2s^1$	$2s^2$
	$1s^2$	$1s^2$

B	C	N	O	F	Ne	Na	Mg
$2p^1$	$2p^2$	$2p^3$	$2p^4$	$2p^5$	$2p^6$	$3s^1$	$3s^2$
$2s^2$	$2s^2$	$2s^2$	$2s^2$	$2s^2$	$2s^2$	$2p^6$	$2p^6$

Al	Si	P	S	Cl	Ar	K	Ca
$3p^1$	$3p^2$	$3p^3$	$3p^4$	$3p^5$	$3p^6$	$4s^1$	$4s^2$
$3s^2$	$3s^2$	$3s^2$	$3s^2$	$3s^2$	$3s^2$	$3p^6$	$3p^6$

V	Cr	Mn	Fe	Co	Ni	Cu	Zn	Ga	Ge	As	Se	Br	Kr	Rb	Sr
$4s^2$	$4s^1$	$4s^2$	$4s^2$	$4s^2$	$4s^2$	$4s^1$	$4s^2$	$4p^1$	$4p^2$	$4p^3$	$4p^4$	$4p^5$	$4p^6$	$5s^1$	$5s^2$
$3d^3$	$3d^5$	$3d^5$	$3d^6$	$3d^7$	$3d^8$	$3d^{10}$	$3d^{10}$	$4s^2$	$4s^2$	$4s^2$	$4s^2$	$4s^2$	$4s^2$	$4p^6$	$4p^6$

Nb	Mo	Tc	Ru	Rh	Pd	Ag	Cd	In	Sn	Sb	Te	I	Xe	Cs	Ba
$5s^1$	$5s^1$	$5s^1$	$5s^1$	$5s^1$		$5s^1$	$5s^2$	$5p^1$	$5p^2$	$5p^3$	$5p^4$	$5p^5$	$5p^6$	$6s^1$	$6s^2$
$4d^4$	$4d^5$	$4d^6$	$4d^7$	$4d^8$	$4d^{10}$	$4d^{10}$	$4d^{10}$	$5s^2$	$5s^2$	$5s^2$	$5s^2$	$5s^2$	$5s^2$	$5p^6$	$5p^6$

Ta	W	Re	Os	Ir	Pt	Au	Hg	Tl	Pb	Bi	Po	At	Rn	Fr	Ra
$6s^2$	$6s^2$	$6s^2$	$6s^2$	$6s^2$	$6s^1$	$6s^1$	$6s^2$	$6p^1$	$6p^2$	$6p^3$	$6p^4$	$6p^5$	$6p^6$	$7s^1$	$7s^2$
$5d^3$	$5d^4$	$5d^5$	$5d^6$	$5d^7$	$5d^9$	$5d^{10}$	$5d^{10}$	$6s^2$	$6s^2$	$6s^2$	$6s^2$	$6s^2$	$6s^2$	$6p^6$	$6p^6$
$4f^{14}$	$4f^{14}$	$4f^{14}$	$4f^{14}$	$4f^{14}$	$4f^{14}$	$4f^{14}$	$4f^{14}$	$5d^{10}$	$5d^{10}$	$5d^{10}$	$5d^{10}$	$5d^{10}$	$5d^{10}$	$6s^2$	$6s^2$

Table 1-2 Designations of Element Groups

	s1	s2	p1	p2	p3	p4	p5	p6	d1	d2	d3	d4	d5	d6	d7	d8	d9	d10	f1	f2	f3	f4	f5	f6	f7	f8	f9	f10	f11	f12	f13	f14
1	1 H $1s^1$	2 He $1s^2$																														
2	3 Li $2s^1$	4 Be $2s^2$	5 B $2p^1$	6 C $2p^2$	7 N $2p^3$	8 O $2p^4$	9 F $2p^5$	10 Ne $2p^6$																								
3	11 Na $3s^1$	12 Mg $3s^2$	13 Al $3p^1$	14 Si $3p^2$	15 P $3p^3$	16 S $3p^4$	17 Cl $3p^5$	18 Ar $3p^6$																								
4	19 K $4s^1$	20 Ca $4s^2$	31 Ga $4p^1$	32 Ge $4p^2$	33 As $4p^3$	34 Se $4p^4$	35 Br $4p^5$	36 Kr $4p^6$	21 Sc $3d^1$	22 Ti $3d^2$	23 V $3d^3$	24 Cr $3d^4$	25 Mn $3d^5$	26 Fe $3d^6$	27 Co $3d^7$	28 Ni $3d^8$	29 Cu $3d^9$	30 Zn $3d^{10}$														
5	37 Rb $5s^1$	38 Sr $5s^2$	49 In $5p^1$	50 Sn $5p^2$	51 Sb $5p^3$	52 Te $5p^4$	53 I $5p^5$	54 Xe $5p^6$	39 Y $4d^1$	40 Zr $4d^2$	41 Nb $4d^3$	42 Mo $4d^4$	43 Tc $4d^5$	44 Ru $4d^6$	45 Rh $4d^7$	46 Pd $4d^8$	47 Ag $4d^9$	48 Cd $4d^{10}$														
6	55 Cs $6s^1$	56 Ba $6s^2$	81 Tl $6p^1$	82 Pb $6p^2$	83 Bi $6p^3$	84 Po $6p^4$	85 At $6p^5$	86 Rn $6p^6$	71 Lu $5d^1$	72 Hf $5d^2$	73 Ta $5d^3$	74 W $5d^4$	75 Re $5d^5$	76 Os $5d^6$	77 Ir $5d^7$	78 Pt $5d^8$	79 Au $5d^9$	80 Hg $5d^{10}$	57 La $4f^1$	58 Ce $4f^2$	59 Pr $4f^3$	60 Nd $4f^4$	61 Pm $4f^5$	62 Sm $4f^6$	63 Eu $4f^7$	64 Gd $4f^8$	65 Tb $4f^9$	66 Dy $4f^{10}$	67 Ho $4f^{11}$	68 Er $4f^{12}$	69 Tm $4f^{13}$	70 Yb $4f^{14}$
7	87 Fr $7s^1$	88 Ra $7s^2$							103 Lw $6d^1$										89 Ac $5f^1$	90 Th $5f^2$	91 Pa $5f^3$	92 U $5f^4$	93 Np $5f^5$	94 Pu $5f^6$	95 Am $5f^7$	96 Cm $5f^8$	97 Bk $5f^9$	98 Cf $5f^{10}$	99 Es $5f^{11}$	100 Fm $5f^{12}$	101 Md $5f^{13}$	102 No $5f^{14}$

the **p,** early **d,** and very early **f** elements is the group number plus 2. Sanderson has made some interesting alternative suggestions for classification (Preface Reference 1).

Use will still be made, however, of terms like "alkaline-earths" (column **s2** without helium), "transition elements" (**d** elements, sometimes excluding **d10**), and "rare-earths" (**4f** elements plus lutetium and possibly yttrium). In the IUPAC recommendations (Preface Reference 3), the ACS has inserted a helpful recommendation for "lanthanoid" to replace "lanthanide" with its unfortunate ending.

Where we speak of "heavy" or "light" **p** elements, for instance, the meaning is clear. "Early" and "late" **d** elements will mean those on the left and right sides, respectively, of the periodic charts generally used.

1-2 ATOMIC ENERGY LEVELS

Another perspective on the order of filling for the various shells and subshells is given by Fig. 1–1. Each subshell is represented as having a single energy level in each atom, with no allowance for spin-spin or spin-orbit interactions or other complications in the numerous levels actually observed spectroscopically. This leaves us with the major effects due to the attraction of the electrons by the nucleus and to the interelectronic repulsions. Theoretical calculations[2-3a] give approximate energy levels and qualitatively correct trends, but with the abrupt drops, especially for d and f levels, coming too late. (More elaborate calculations have now been carried out for the lightest atoms.)[4] This figure (in the upper and middle sections) is therefore keyed mainly to actual levels in the **sl** and **d9** elements. These alkali and coinage metals have numerous accurately known states[1a] in which the one outer s electron is excited, leaving the other electrons in an inert-gas structure or a similar structure plus a closed d subshell. In these states, only one small complication remains: the spin of the excited electron can add to or subtract from the orbital angular momentum of the same electron. The resulting two energy levels (high J and low J) at each configuration are simply averaged in the figure. Values for the other much more complicated elements are chosen for continuity, with guidance from the theoretical calculations[2-3a] and, to a lesser extent, from other spectra and chemical properties.

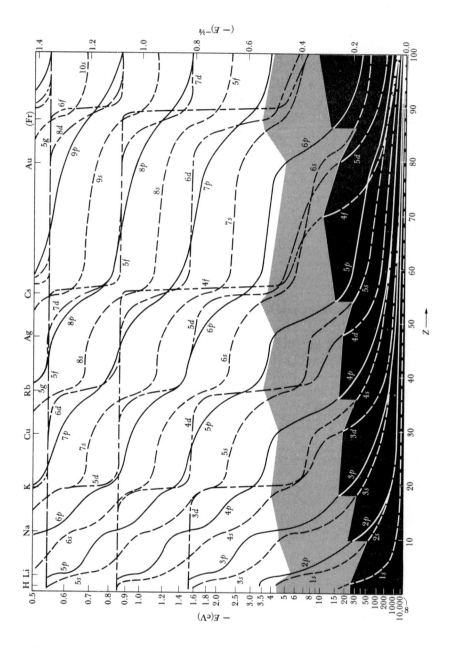

Fig. 1–1. Approximate energy levels for neutral atoms. White background, normally empty subshells; gray background, valence subshells; black background, normally full subshells.

The energies of the upper normally empty levels can be defined as the energies required to ionize the *excited* electron from those levels in the *neutral* atom, leaving the other electrons unchanged in the *ground*-state configuration of the *ion*. The energies of the lowest, normally full levels, in contrast, are the ones required to ionize an electron from the *ground*-state configuration of a *neutral* atom, leaving the *ion excited* due to the low-lying vacancy. For this part of the diagram, the energies are derived from experimental X-ray results[5-6] for most of the elements since the complications are not too burdensome.

The middle section of Fig. 1–1 represents the valence electrons. Ionization of many of these can proceed from the ground-state configuration of the neutral atom to the ground-state configuration of the ion. Where the occupancy of an orbital changes from one electron to none, the process is like that in the upper levels; where it changes from two to one, it is like that in the lower ones. This region thus provides some continuity of definitions and gives such a graph more unity than might at first seem possible.

Several patterns in the trends of energy levels stand out clearly, and reasonable interpretations of these are certainly required for any genuine understanding of periodicity. The general decrease of orbital energies with increasing atomic number is of course expected from the increasing positive charge on the nucleus.

But why do the $4s$ and $4p$ levels, for example, drop long before the $4d$ and especially $4f$ levels? We recall that s electrons have maximum radial motion but zero orbital angular momentum, while the f electrons have minimum radial motion and maximum angular momentum. The s electrons therefore "penetrate" any underlying shells most effectively and feel the full nuclear charge during part of their travels.[7-8] The $4f$ orbitals in the light atoms, however, are almost entirely outside of the filled electron shells. As we go from one element to the next, then, we add not only a proton to the nucleus but also an electron to an orbital relatively near the nucleus. We say that the added electrons "shield" or "screen" the outer orbitals, especially those with high angular momentum, until higher atomic numbers are reached. Then these orbitals also feel the "penetration" effect and the lowest ones begin to be filled.

Just *before* the first abrupt drop in the f levels, penetration brings even the $7p$ orbitals temporarily to lower energies than those of the $4f$. At the *highest* atomic numbers in the lower, filled levels, however, we find the "normal" order restored: . . . $4s$, $4p$, $4d$, $4f$, $5s$, $5p$, and so on. The penetration effect, though still significant here, cannot distinguish so sharply between f and s electrons (to continue just one example) when both are in inner orbitals subject to large "effective" nuclear charges. This is simply because their shielding electrons now carry a smaller fraction of the (large) total charge.

At the intermediate atomic numbers, then, including those where the f orbitals are just being filled, the increases of effective nuclear charge are *relatively* more important for f than for s orbitals; this partly explains the faster decline in the f levels and the crossing of the two types. In the same way, although less rapidly, the valence d levels fall below the s types in the transition elements. In all cases, however, there is a partial pause in the decline of energies while the orbitals are being filled. This reflects, as the reader may have anticipated, a partial shielding of electrons by the others added at similar distances from the nucleus.

Another way of understanding the relative constancy of the $6s$ levels in the rare earths, for instance, is to note that the added $4f$ electrons are mainly inside the $6s$ orbitals, and the former are therefore fairly effective in shielding the latter. This implies a greater absolute, as well as greater percentage, increase of effective nuclear charge acting on the f orbitals than on the s orbitals as the atomic number increases.

Among the unfilled orbitals we notice that the f types are either the most constant or falling the most steeply, that they all fall together (with $5f$, for example, going to the energy vacated by the $4f$), and that when they are not falling, each one has almost exactly the energy of a hydrogen level. The same patterns appear less clearly in the d and p orbitals. These interesting trends in the nonvalence levels are less important for most ordinary chemistry, but were predicted for the f case by Mayer,[9] who also gives a qualitative explanation.

One of the important points in all of this is that, contrary to the impression sometimes given, the order of energy levels is not constant.[10] It is possible, however, to use well-known mnemonics[10] with fair accuracy for the "order of filling" of valence electrons in neutral atoms.

We now wish to offer a comparatively simple interpretation of the seemingly chaotic ground-state configurations in the valence shells of the **d** and **f** elements, using Fig. 1–2. In addition to the larger penetration or shielding effects already discussed, we now need to consider the effect of pairing, that is, putting two electrons into the same orbital. Two such electrons will have greater mutual repulsions and higher energies than if they were not paired. This is partly due to the Pauli principle, as pointed out by Dickens and Linnett.[11] We therefore have to revise the common idea that electrons inherently tend to pair up. Such pairing, though common, is favored only when the pairing energy is not great enough to force promotion of one electron to the next higher vacant orbital.

It is convenient for clarity in the diagram and does not lead to erroneous conclusions to assign all of the extra energy of pairing in each orbital to just one electron, so that the other is unchanged, regardless of pairing. In Fig. 1–2 this procedure gives us two lines to represent the energies of individual electrons in each subshell. The lower line is used until the subshell is half

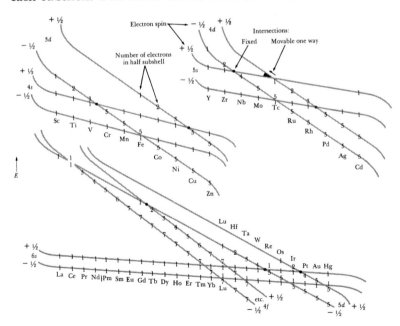

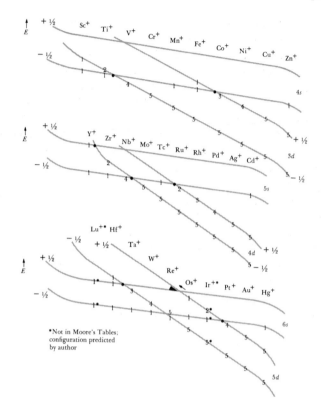

Fig. 1–2. Schematic interpretation of electron configurations for transition and rare-earth elements in terms of the intra-orbital repulsion and the trends in subshell energies.

full, after which the upper line is also used. For each element, then, we merely give the outer electrons the lowest energies available. In this way we can rationalize, for example, the configuration s^2d^2 for zirconium and sd^4 for niobium, since the lower d line is assumed to cross the upper s line between these two elements. We see that this does not always lead to exactly half-full (for example, d^5) or full (or empty) subshells, although these structures will occur relatively often just because some additional energy is required to go beyond them. In the rest of the book, this understanding will be assumed when speaking of some tendency toward, or extra stability in, configurations whose subshells are precisely half full or full.

It may be objected that the d and f levels of neutral atoms in Fig. 1–2 are higher (in comparison to s) or intersect the s type later than in Fig. 1–1. The previous figure is based on energy differences between neutral atoms and unipositive ions and is therefore influenced somewhat by a net positive charge. As seen here and below, such a net charge lowers the energies of s orbitals less than those of the d and f ones. Figure 1–2 is intended only to lead to the correct configuration within each atom.

This model still does not consider magnetic, relativistic, or other effects. It may not account for the structure of cerium, or those of protactinium, uranium, and neptunium (not drawn), although the interpretation of the spectra of these f elements is quite difficult and uncertain.

Figure 1–3 gives further information on the effect of charge and on precise energy levels (derived from spectroscopy) in ions whose neutral forms were too complicated to represent adequately in Fig. 1–1. Let us note first that the ionization energy of Mg^+, for instance, is numerically equal to the electron affinity of Mg^{2+}. The latter designation is used here because of the greater familiarity (to chemists) of the fully ionized forms. We are thus viewing the energy levels as the energies released when a free electron enters various empty orbitals of the ion. We choose the ions with inert-gas structures or full d subshells both because some of these are important chemically and because the corresponding energy levels (with only one valence electron added) are comparatively simple.

It is important to note that the energies plotted have been *divided* by the square of the ionic charge in order to eliminate the main anticipated effect (in hydrogen-like atoms) on *outer* electrons. Therefore, the curves that rise to the right do not stand for rising energies, but only for energies that are falling less rapidly than expected in hydrogen-like atoms. A few interpolations have been used.

It is interesting to see the increasing complexity as we go to the heavier isoelectronic series. In most cases, the s and p orbitals show a decreasing effect of penetration at higher nuclear charges, as explained earlier. The d and f orbitals, however, are often pulled down strongly in energy by the first increases of charge; further increases then show a reduced effect of penetra-

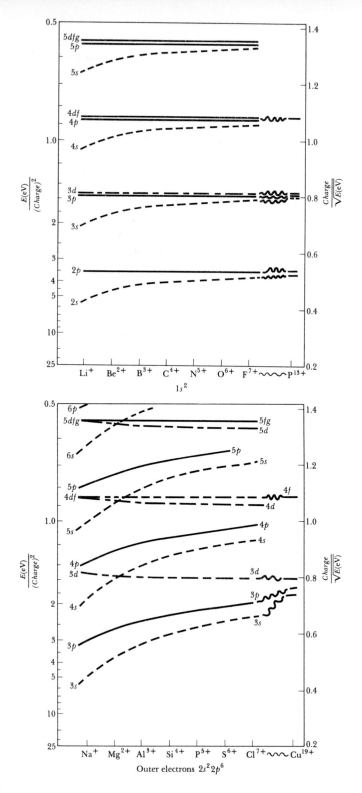

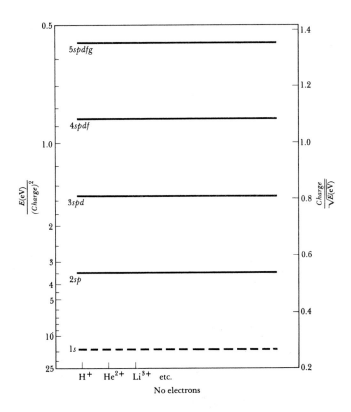

tion. A slight initial drop may also be barely detected at Be^{2+} for the p orbitals. Obviously, a small space would not suffice for even qualitative explanations of the details in these and other trends that the reader will find. Equally clearly, however, thinking about these patterns should strengthen our understanding of periodicity and much of chemistry.

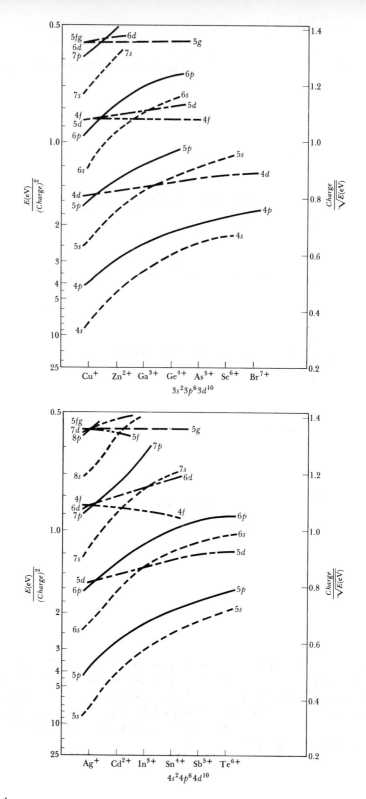

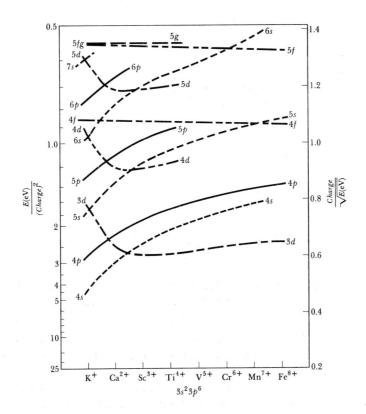

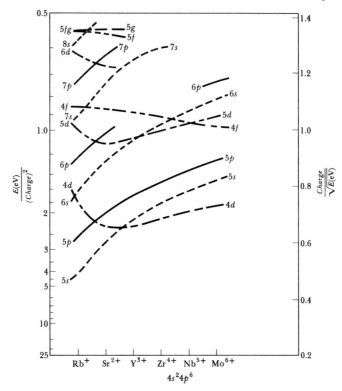

1-3 THE 8-ELECTRON RULE IN MOLECULES CONTAINING p ELEMENTS

Inert-gas rules have long had an honorable place in chemistry. Since bonding electrons in typical molecules often occur in pairs, it has become habitual to think of all outer electrons, shared and unshared, as tending to pair up; the familiar octet has thus been viewed as four pairs. Unfortunately, problems have appeared even in instances (O_2) that formerly seemed to illustrate the octet or inert-gas rule. We would thus have expected N_2, O_2, and F_2 to have the following structures (I, II, and III), where each arrow represents the spin vector of one outer electron:

In this structure for oxygen, each atom would share two pairs of electrons with the other atom, and would have two pairs

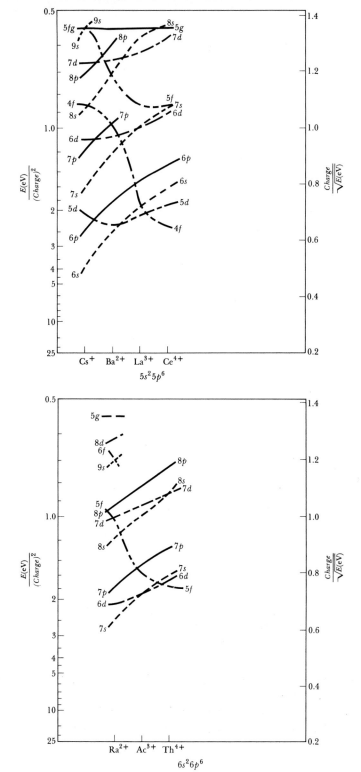

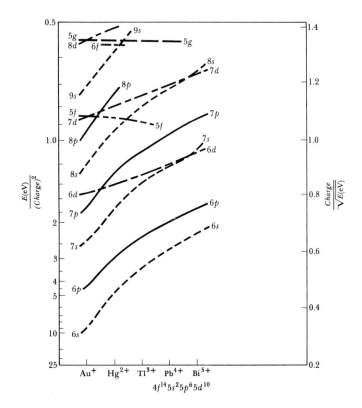

Fig. 1–3. Actual energy levels of one electron added to ions shown; average of high J and low J states.

all its own, in addition. Oxygen would therefore be diamagnetic, contrary to observation.

Molecular orbital theory deals successfully with these problems and with spectroscopic data, but with the use of a less pictorial model and without consideration (in first approximation) of electron correlation effects that determine relative positions of the electrons. Linnett's double quartet model[11b] has advantages in these and some other respects, although it is less general, and will be discussed here as a tentative but interesting variation of the 8-electron or octet rule. Certainly no one way of describing molecular structure, however, has yet won or is immediately likely to win universal and exclusive acceptance.

A detailed consideration of the Pauli exclusion principle in modern form shows that, even without including electrostatic repulsion, the wave function of a group of electrons, all confined to the same region of space and having the same spin, favors maximum separation among them; electrons having opposite spins are, in the same way, brought together. Due to Coulombic forces, the energy in the former case will clearly be reduced while in the latter case it will be raised.[11a] This difference is at the root of the so-called (and often seemingly mysterious) "exchange energies."

The Pauli principle alone would thus cause a quartet of unpaired electrons to have the greatest probability of occurring at the corners of a tetrahedron. Two such quartets, with electron spins in opposite directions, would form two separate tetrahedral electron clouds. The Pauli effect, or spin correlation, would tend to put these two into coincidence; the electrostatic effect, or charge correlation, into anticoincidence. In an atom like neon, then, these two quartets are not strongly correlated. The cubic close-packed structure of the solid noble gases, except for helium, does provide evidence, however, for some pairing. This structure permits both types (spin up and spin down) of the tetrahedrally arranged electron sets in neighboring atoms to avoid each other better than would the hexagonal arrangement. The hexagonal close-packed structure, as in solid helium, would otherwise be favored by the London (van der Waals) forces operating over the slightly shorter distances between atoms in alternate hexagonal layers.

Before examining molecular structure on this basis, we can suggest a partial but fundamental interpretation of the usually unexplained relative stability of the noble-gas octet. We ask why argon, for example, is so much less reactive than calcium, zinc, or ytterbium, all of which have all subshells, but no outer shells, either completely full or empty. (Thus, in argon the $3s$ and $3p$

are fully occupied and the $3d$ is empty, so that the third shell is not complete.) We can see in Table 1–1 that only the noble gases have outer shells with as many as *two* subshells complete. These two subshells overlap in space better than, say, the $3p$ and $4s$ in different shells of calcium. This spatial overlapping is required for a strong spin correlation effect or quartet formation, and the concomitant reduction of internal electrostatic repulsion helps account for the properties of the noble gases.

In methane, water, and so on, the two quartets are of course brought into strong coincidence by the attraction of the hydrogen or other nuclei. That is, the shared electrons, whether spinning one way or the other, are both pulled into the regions between the hydrogens and the other nucleus. In water, the two fixed corners of the tetrahedra will tend to restrict the motion of the unshared electrons, although the shared ones will still be the more localized. In HF, only one corner is fixed, and the two tetrahedral quartets should be free to rotate fairly independently around the H—F axis.

This point of view accounts for the approximately tetrahedral angles found in many molecules, although up to this point in our discussion it has not led to testable predictions different from earlier ones. Without using the language of hybridization, this approach gives its own justification for the type of orbitals represented by the sp^3 hybrid. As Pople has clearly shown,[13] if all such orbitals are equally occupied, it does not matter mathematically whether the complete antisymmetric (determinantal) wave function is based on ordinary atomic orbitals or on these localized, hybrid, "equivalent" orbitals.

Let us now apply the double quartet model to the diatomic molecules of **2p** elements. The structures of F_2 and N_2 can be written as before.

(IV)   (V)

Structures such as IV and V are ruled out because they would place an entire quartet (spin ↑) on one side of each atom rather than tetrahedrally distributed around it. Thus the pairing of all electrons in N_2 and F_2 is predicted (structures I and III). In O_2, however, structure VI is permitted and is favored by its provi-

(VI)

sion of two unpaired electrons (7↓ minus 5↑) with no tetra-hedra (quartets) in coincidence, thus reducing the total electro-static repulsion energy. The four bonding electrons can be counted as one pair and two singles, or a kind of one and two halves bond. The molecular orbital picture[14a] might be con-sidered as yielding a similar bond order, though it could also be dubbed three minus two halves. The O_2 structure II would have its 12 electrons more nearly in coincidence. Considering this structure to have a normal double bond and identifying it with the $^1\Sigma$ state of spectroscopy, we conclude that its energy is 38 kcal/mole above the ground state.[11b]

The coincidence effect is brought out more clearly in Fig. 1–4, which includes structures of a few interesting compounds. Here the electrons that are not in coincidence are printed black, while the pairs or quartets that do tend to coincide are white. Some intermediate pairs are shown in both colors. A number of old problems are immediately cleared up without either resonance or molecular orbital theory. An example is the great strength of the C=O bond in CO_2, compared to the bond in aldehydes or ketones. The lack of coincidence of the 16 va-lence electrons in CO_2 corresponds to a stabilization (or reso-nance) energy of 30 kcal/mole based on Equation 1–1:

$$2(CH_3)_2CO \rightarrow CO_2 + C(CH_3)_4 + 30 \text{ kcal} \qquad (1\text{–}1)$$

A similar effect for the 18 ring electrons in benzene as compared to ethylene and ethane (not shown) corresponds to a stabilization energy of 36 kcal/mole. In B_2H_6, of course, we have full coinci-dence and two 3-center bonds, as in other models.[14b]

Looking at the compounds of nitrogen, we find a ready in-terpretation of the lack of dimerization of NO. N_2O_2 would have all electrons paired without any compensating gain in number of bonding electrons. The dissociation of N_2F_4 ($K \approx 10^{-7}$) to

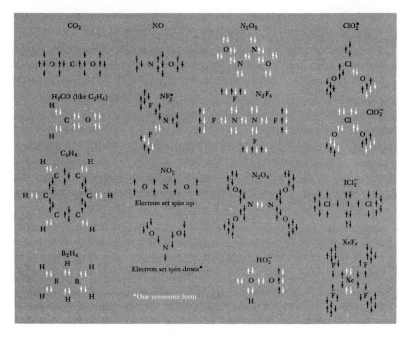

Fig. 1–4. Some double-quartet structures.

NF_2 is similarly promoted, though less drastically because the difference in number of coincident electrons is less.

NO_2 illustrates another effect; it should be less stable than NO since the two sets of electrons favor different molecular geometries. The 8 electrons with spin vector up tend to form a linear set of tetrahedra joined by edges, but the other 9 electrons would find a more stable arrangement in an angular molecule, as illustrated. In other words, either the tetrahedra must have considerable distortion, or the bonding electrons must stay rather far from the best positions between the nuclei. In N_2O_4 this problem is not present but the central bonding pair must be brought into coincidence. The result may help explain the equilibrium between monomer and dimer, although the isoelectronic $C_2O_4^{2-}$ does not dissociate so easily. (In solids, however, this ion is stabilized by cations and, in solution, by solvation.) Some further interesting features of N_2O_4 are discussed by Bent.[15a]

For a few molecules, including NO_2 and ClO_2, the resonance concept is still required in order to understand the symmetry of bonding. Thus the motion of the electrons in ClO_2 cannot allow only a single bond from chlorine to one oxygen and a $1\frac{1}{2}$ bond to the other; instead, each bond must have an intermediate character.

It is interesting to see that the addition of one electron to ClO_2 would cause a drastic rearrangement, with quite a few electrons becoming paired in ClO_2^-. This certainly may help to explain the relative stability of the neutral molecule. We may in fact begin to wonder whether there should not therefore be many more molecules having an odd number of electrons. The reader may wish to diagram the quite unstable ClO_3, for example. This compares to ClO_2 as NO_2 compares to NO. In other words, the two sets of electrons in ClO_3 must again favor different geometries, this time one planar and one pyramidal. We should hasten to add that much of the instability of all the chlorine oxides does not refer to dimerization but to decomposition, although the present discussion remains relevant.

In the example of HO_2^-, we can see that loss of a proton often (not in CH_4 for example) permits some disengagement of electron tetrahedra. This could be one of the factors promoting acidity in hydroxy compounds.

In ICl_2^-, quadrupole-coupling data and bond distances argue against heavy contributions of p-d π (often redundantly called p_π-d_π) bonding, and the structure in Fig. 1–4 is a reasonable alternative. Similar one-electron bonds in XeF_2 and other noble-gas fluorides are consonant with their modest stabilities. In square planar XeF_4 or ICl_4^-, each quartet would have to be arranged approximately in a square with two bonding and two nonbonding electrons. The molecules and quartets could not be tetrahedral without making all the central atom valence electrons bonding and exceeding the octets of the outer atoms. This would be especially prohibited with the fluorides.[16–18]

Where the double quartet model is not applicable, the more general nonpairing approach is often useful. In $B(CH_3)_3$, for example, the bonding electrons around the boron are arranged in triangles, rather than in tetrahedra. In PCl_5, however, it is not so clear from first principles whether we should invoke two quintets of electrons or two quartets. The first calls for a d orbital and the second calls for resonance; both may be reasonable.

Linnett has even carried this idea over to the hydrogen bond. HF_2^- might therefore be written as in Structure VII, al-

$$\begin{array}{ccc} \uparrow\downarrow\downarrow & & \uparrow\uparrow\downarrow \\ \uparrow \ F \uparrow H \downarrow \ F \ \downarrow \\ \uparrow\downarrow\downarrow & & \uparrow\uparrow\downarrow \end{array}$$

(VII)

though we would not necessarily have to believe that this co-valent form is more important than the ionic. In both this structure and ICl_2^-, given previously, the two valence electrons have opposite spins and therefore no strong angular correlation.

Some writers have pointed out that species like the last several ones mentioned here could be covered better by a "rule of two" than by the older "rule of eight." This is true, but such a less-restrictive rule, accepting any number of *pairs* of electrons, is also less informative. Thus it would permit the existence of PH, CH_2, NF_5 and H_4O as stable molecules. Of course, the double quartet (or triplet, quintet, and so on) model could also be generalized too far in this direction.

Where the 8-electron rule in compounds of **p** elements is or appears to be violated, as well as where it is not, the proposals of Gillespie and Nyholm have usually permitted good predictions of molecular geometry.[19] In this model, the outer electrons are usually paired and both the bonding and nonbonding pairs repel each other, but the repulsions decrease in the order: nonbonding to nonbonding; nonbonding to bonding; bonding to bonding. This is simply because the bonding electrons are more effectively neutralized by nuclei on two sides.

This model will not be developed here in detail, but the reader may be able to satisfy himself of some of its interesting predictions. The tetrahedral geometry of methane is of course predicted, as are the somewhat less than tetrahedral angles in ammonia and water. Structures based on a trigonal bipyramid (considering bonding and nonbonding electrons together) include PCl_5, SF_4, ClF_3 (a T-shaped molecule), and linear I_3^- or XeF_2. In some of the cases just mentioned, however, not all ambiguity is removed. XeF_6 should presumably not be a regular octahedron but should have the unshared pair on one side, according to this model. The only clearly incorrect predictions from this model that are known to the writer involve the gaseous alkaline-earth halide molecules. Some of these are bent, whereas all would have been linear according to *most* present theories.

Before this section is concluded, it seems appropriate to point out that the 8-electron rule could perhaps be called the 18-electron rule in the case of **4p** and **5p** elements, and the 32-electron rule in the case of **6p** elements, if we wish to count *all* the electrons beyond the previous noble gas, not only the valence electrons. The terms "inert-gas" or "noble-gas" rule would also be good but, like the above, do not distinguish the subject of this section from that of the next.

1-4   THE 18-ELECTRON RULE IN MOLECULES CONTAINING d ELEMENTS

It is evident that no reasonable modification of simple rules of the type discussed in the previous section would describe well the arrangement of d electrons in a series of compounds such as $MnSO_4$, $FeSO_4$, $CoSO_4$, $NiSO_4$, $CuSO_4$, $ZnSO_4$ where there is a constant oxidation state rather than a constant number of valence electrons. Also, many aspects of the periodicity of these elements are given later. We will therefore turn our attention to a type of compound which has aroused much recent interest and which happens to show a striking periodicity of formula, related to another kind of "inert-gas rule." [18, 20]

A few of the compounds under discussion, or their ions, are listed in Table 1–3. Many of them have bonds from metal atoms to carbon atoms in unsaturated groups. Some have metal-metal bonds or bonds to heavy **p** elements, whose empty outer d orbitals give them a somewhat unsaturated character. In a way, the table actually underemphasizes periodicity; in series like $Fe(CO)_5$, $Ru(CO)_5$, and $Os(CO)_5$, only one member has been given, for the sake of conciseness. In many cases, substances derived from other elements of a given **d** family and analogous to those included are known; in many other cases, however, they are not yet known.

One notable feature is that, whereas other parts of transition-element chemistry often show nearly constant coordination numbers but variable d orbital occupancy, here we find little standardization of the former with considerable rigidity in the latter. All of the complexes listed can be considered to have as many valence electrons, shared or not, around the metal atom as

Table 1-3 Some Series of Complexes Illustrating the 18-Electron Rule

gr	d3	d4	d5	d6	d7	d8	d9	d10
	$V(CN)_5 NO^{5-}$	$Cr(CN)_5 NO^{4-}$	$Mn(CN)_5 NO^{3-}$	$Fe(CN)_5 NO^{2-}$				
			$MnCO(NO)_3$	$Fe(CO)_2 (NO)_2$	$Co(CO)_3 NO$	$Ni(CO)_4$		
		$Cr(CN)_6^{6-}$	$Mn(CN)_6^{5-}$	$Fe(CN)_6^{4-}$	$Co(CN)_6^{3-}$	$Ni(CN)_5^{3-}$ / $Ni(CN)_4^{4-}$	$Cu(CN)_4^{3-}$	$Zn(CN)_4^{2-}$
		$Cr(CNR)_6$	$Mn(CNR)_6^+$	$Fe(CNR)_6^{2+}$	$Co(CNR)_5^+$	$Ni(CNR)_4$	$Cu(CNR)_4^+$	
	$V(CO)_6^-$	$Cr(CO)_6$	$Mn(CO)_6^+$	$Fe(CO)_6^{2+}$		$Ni(CO)_4$		
		$Cr(CO)_5^{2-}$	$Mn(CO)_5^-$	$Fe(CO)_5$	$Co(CO)_4^-$	$Ni(CO)_3^{2-}$		
			$Mn_2 (CO)_{10}$	$Fe(CO)_4^{2-}$	$Co_2 (CO)_8$			
				$Fe_2 (CO)_9$ / $Fe_2 (CO)_8^{2-}$				
	$TaCpd_2 H_3$	$WCpd_2 H_3^+$ / $WCpd_2 H_2$	$ReCpd_2 H_2^+$ / $ReCpd_2 H$	$OsCpd_2$	$IrCpd_2^+$			
	$VCpd(CO)_4$	$CrCpd(CO)_4^+$	$MnCpd(CO)_3$	$FeCpd(CO)_3^+$	$CoCpd(CO)_2$			
	$VCpd(CO)_3^{2-}$	$CrCpd(CO)_3^-$		$FeCpd(CO)_2^-$				
		$MoBzn_2$	$TcBzn_2^+$	$RuBzn_2^{2+}$	$RhBzn_2^{3+}$			
			$MnCpdBzn$	$FeCpdBzn^+$	$CoCpdBzn_2^{2+}$			
				$FeCpdCpd$	$CoCpdCbd$	$NiCpdAll$		
		$Cr_2 Cpd_2 (CO)_6$		$Fe_2 Cpd_2 (CO)_4$		$Ni_2 Cpd_2 (CO)_2$		
		$CrCpd(CO)_3 X$		$FeCpd(CO)_2 X$		$NiCpdCOX$		
	$VCht(CO)_3$	$CrCht(CO)_3^+$ / $CrBzn(CO)_3$	$MnBzn(CO)_3^+$ / $MnCpd(CO)_3$	$FeCpd(CO)_3^+$ / $FeBtd(CO)_3$	$CoAll(CO)_3$			

Cr(CO)$_4$(PR$_3$)$_2$	Fe(CO)$_3$(PR$_3$)$_2$	Ni(CO)$_2$(PR$_3$)$_2$
	FeH$_2$Dipn$_2$	CoHDipn$_2$	NiDipn$_2$
	RuTtsnCl$_2$	PdTrsnCl$_2$	CdDisnCl$_2$

Miscellaneous interesting examples:

–TiCpd$_2$(CO)$_2$	Cr·Dipn$_3$	ReEtn$_2$(CO)$_4^+$	(Os(CO)$_4$)$_3$	Rh$_2$(CN)$_8^{8-}$	Ni(PF$_3$)$_4$
VCpd$_2$(CO)$_2^+$	Cr(CO)$_3$(NH$_3$)$_3$	Tc$_2$Cpd$_4$	FeH(CO)$_5^+$	Co$_2$(CN)$_{10}^{6-}$	Ni$_2$AcnCpd$_2$
NbCpd$_2$Br$_3$	WCpd$_2$H$_2$BF$_3$	ReAcn$_2$PR$_3$Cl	Fe$_3$(CO)$_{11}^{2-}$	Co$_2$Acn(CO)$_6$	NiCpdNO
	W(CN)$_8^{4-}$	Re(CN)$_8$OH^{2-}	Fe(NO)$_3^-$	CoNOR$_2$NCS)$_2$	PtH$_2$(PR$_3$)$_3$
		ReH$_3$(PR$_3$)$_4$	Fe(NO)$_3$Cl	IrH$_3$(PR$_3$)$_3$	
		GeH$_2$(Mn(CO)$_5$)$_2$		Ga(Co(CO)$_4$)$_3$	

AgDisn$_2^+$	Hg(CNR)$_2$Cl$_2$
Cu(PR$_3$)$_4^+$	TlCpd—
CuAcnCl$_2^-$	
CuCpdPR$_3$	

n (no. of contributed electrons)

7 Cht = π-C$_7$H$_7$, cycloheptatrienyl (radical) or deriv.
6 Bzn = π-C$_6$H$_6$, benzene or deriv.
5 Cpd = π-C$_5$H$_5$, cyclopentadienyl or deriv.
4 Cbd = π-C$_4$R$_4$, cyclobutadiene deriv.
4 Btd = π-C$_4$H$_6$, butadiene or deriv.
3 All = π-C$_3$H$_5$, allyl or deriv.
2 Etn = π-C$_2$H$_4$, ethylene or deriv.
1 R = CH$_3$, σ-C$_5$H$_5$, C$_6$H$_5$, etc.
4 Acn = π-C$_2$R$_2$, acetylene deriv.

n
0 BF$_3$
1 CN, H, OH, X = Cl, Br, I, R, SR, SiR$_3$, Hg/2
2 CO, CNR, NCR, NH$_3$, PR$_3$, AsR$_3$, SbCl$_3$, SR$_2$, etc.
3 NO, R$_2$NCS$_2$
4 Dipn = a diphosphine, e.g., 1,2-C$_2$H$_4$(PR$_2$)$_2$ or 1,2-C$_6$H$_4$(PR$_2$)$_2$. Disn = a diarsine.
6 Trsn = a triarsine.
8 Ttsn = a tetraarsine.
1 per M for M$_2$ (dimer with M—M bond)
2 per M in cyclo-M$_3$ (3 metal—metal bonds)

Some common abbreviations of organic ligands are avoided for the following reasons: The use of only small letters, as in Cocpdbtd, can obviously be ambiguous and distracting. Addition of parentheses would increase clarity, but with better symbols, would not be needed and, as in [Fe(CO)$_2$(cpd)]$_2$, may be awkward. The use of only capitals promotes the same ambiguity and may suggest elements, for example, tritium, hydrogen, and fluorine for THF of tetrahydrofuran. Fortunately, all of these problems are easily overcome by the adoption of abbreviations like Cpd, Thf, and Acac, hereby recommended, or even shorter ones where confusion with elements can be minimized.

the next noble gas would have; with the outer ten d, two s, and six p electrons, this number is 18. To arrive at this number we add together the following: 1 for each univalent group (H, halogen, CN, and so on), 2 for groups contributing electron pairs (CO, H_2O, Et_3P, and so on), 3 for NO, 5 for cyclopentadienyl radical, and so on. These numbers of electrons, n, from the ligands are added to the group number of the metal (for example, 4 for $d4$) plus 2 (for the s electrons) plus or minus the net negative or positive charge, respectively.

Other ways of counting are certainly permissible, with the same final result. Thus $CoCN(CO)_2NO^-$ could be considered as a combination of Co^{3+}, CN^-, $2CO$, NO^+ and $4e^-$ instead of Co, CN, 2CO, NO and e^-. We would then assume that CN^-, CO and NO^+ (all isoelectronic, incidentally, with the very stable N_2) share two electrons each with the metal atom.

In binuclear complexes like $Co_2(CN)_8^{8-}$ the pair of shared electrons in the single bond between the metal atoms is counted twice and of course the total number finally obtained should be 36 instead of 18. Some exceptions, such as $Co_2Cpd_2(CO)_4$, which would have too many electrons in this counting, are only apparent. This example turns out to be $CoCpd_2^+Co(CO)_4^-$, without a covalent bond between the metal atoms. In $Co_3Bzn_3(CO)_2^+$ the cobalt atoms form a three-membered ring with a benzene molecule attached to each atom and with one CO group above and one below the ring. Here, then, there are three Co—Co bonds, and six cobalt electrons must be counted twice.

Nuclear magnetic resonance, infrared spectra, and other evidence show that $Mn_2Cpd_3(NO)_3$ and $FeCpd_2(CO)_2$ represent another type of the only apparent exceptions. In each case one cyclopentadienyl group is attached to the metal atom at only one carbon (σ-bonded) so that this group must be counted as univalent and not π-bonding. Similarly, the NO group in $Fe(CN)_5NO^{4-}$, $Co(CN)_5NO^{3-}$, $Pt(CN)_5NO^{2-}$, and $Re(CN)_7NO^{3-}$ should probably be counted as univalent; it is then expected to have a lower order N—O bond (having retained more antibonding electrons) and greater N—O distance than otherwise, which ought to be checked. Also, in $Fe(CN)_5NO^{3-}$ magnetic data indicate that the odd electron is mostly on the (NO) nitrogen atom. The NO is therefore counted as a neutral group, sharing just one pair of electrons with the iron. But in $Cr(CN)_5NO^{4-}$, $Cr(CN)_5NO^{3-}$, and $Cr(CN)_5NO^{2-}$ magnetic and spectral data point to changing oxidation states of chromium in conflict with the rule.[21] Actually, there are quite a few reasonably stable π complexes, especially of chromium, with the three t_{2g} nonbonding d orbitals exactly half full, as in ordinary Cr^{3+}.

One important group of genuine exceptions to the 18-electron rule involves many complexes with (1) 16 outer electrons[22a] assignable to the metal, (2) an approximately square-planar geometry, and (3) either some not so strongly π-bonding ligands or heavy or late d (especially $d8$) element central atoms. Examples may include, although not all structures are known: $Fe_2Cl_2(NO)_4$, $Ni_2(CN)_6^{4-}$, $PtHCl(PR_3)_2$, $Pt(NO_2)_4^{2-}$, and $Ni(C_3H_5)_2$.

The rule is particularly strict in carbonyls.[23] $V(CO)_6$, one electron short, is reported to be "extremely reactive," whereas the regular $Cr(CO)_6$, formed from an adjacent central atom, is "extremely stable." Even the light colors of the normal compounds indicate electronic stability, as will be discussed in Chapter 7. Let us understand clearly, however, that the rule can predict only *relative* reactivity and then only with strictly comparable species. Thus $Cr(CN)_6^{6-}$ is highly reactive, but we can predict that $V(CN)_6^{6-}$ or $Mn(CN)_6^{6-}$, violating the rule and not yet known, would be much more reactive. Comparisons involving different coordination numbers or net charges must naturally take account of the other factors introduced.

Since the electronic structures of metallocenes ($MCpd_2$) have been subject to some controversy, further discussion of them is appropriate here. As we go across the $3d$ row of the periodic table we find the following reported temperatures of decomposition or stability:[24]

$TiCpd_2$	$VCpd_2$	$CrCpd_2$	$MnCpd_2$	$FeCpd_2$	$CoCpd_2$	$NiCpd_2$
d 135°	st 300°	st 300°	st 300°	st 400°	st 250°	d 173°

$FeCpd_2$, the only one that can be assigned a noble-gas or 18-electron structure, is the most stable toward heat. It is inert to O_2, HCl, and bases, unlike some of the others, and is the only one that is inert to CO and NO. $FeCpd_2$, $RuCpd_2$, $OsCpd_2$, $MnCpd(CO)_3$, and $CrBzn(CO)_3$, all with noble-gas structures, are alone in showing some typical aromatic substitution reactions *without degradation*. The isoelectronic $CoCpd_2^+$, $RhCpd_2^+$, and $IrCpd_2^+$ are the only metallocene derivatives stable even toward such powerful reagents as ozone, hot concentrated strong bases, hot aqua regia, and hot alkaline peroxide. Other metallocenes and their ions in rows **4d** and **5d** are mostly not even known.

We should also remember that if the 18-electron structures had no special stability at all, we might expect to find only something like $1/18$ or $1/10$ of eligible compounds fitting the rule. Actually, the elements at the extremes of the **d** series do not give rise to conforming compounds as often as those near the middle, as is easily seen in Table 1–3. We recall that to make good hybrid orbitals, the component orbitals must overlap well and not have too discordant energies. In the early **nd** elements ($n = 3, 4,$ or 5) the energy of the $(n + 1)p$ orbitals is somewhat too high.[25] In the late **d** case, the d orbitals are apparently a little too low, in molecular complexes, for the best hybridization and for back donation of d electrons. It also appears that the 18-electron rule works somewhat better for **3d** than for **4d** and **5d** elements.

In the past some writers have interpreted the 18-electron rule to mean that none of these 18 electrons could remain largely with the ligands, which must therefore be highly positive while the central atom acquires an unrealistic negative charge, in violation of the useful Pauling electroneutrality principle.[3b] Others have gone to the opposite extreme, declaring the rule to be merely a formalism without any bearing on structural questions in these cases. In this view, because rough molecular-orbital estimates suggest that only one electron pair goes strongly from each Cpd^- ring to Fe^{2+}, for example, we need a 10-electron rule for the most stable metallocenes. To be consistent, then, we would also need many other "rules" such as a 14-electron rule for $MnCpd(CO)_3$ etc. Likewise, $TlCpd$ has been classified as ionic, although it is volatile and relatively stable and the gaseous monomer fits the 18-electron rule. The argument that its stability depends on favorable crystal packing does not explain the great reactivity to water and air of $RbCpd$, whose cation is the same size as Tl^+.

This discussion has to be much too brief, but surely we can conclude, exactly as in any other branch of chemistry, that there is never a sharp line between ionic and covalent character.[3c] We can also say that the stability of noble-gas electronic structures shows mainly that when all relatively low-energy orbitals are occupied to some extent, consistent with electroneutrality, and when all higher-energy orbitals are empty, then possible reagents find no easy point of attack.[37] Section 8–4 gives some further discussion of π-bonding and back donation of electrons into unsaturated groups.

It should be mentioned that the f elements show little of the behavior described in this section. The f electrons are too well shielded by the outer ones, at least in the lower oxidation states, to participate much in covalent bonding. An example will appear, however, in Section 5–3.

REFERENCES

1. (a) C. E. Moore, *Atomic Energy Levels as Derived from the Analyses of Optical Spectra, Circ. 467* (Washington, D. C.: National Bureau of Standards, 1949–1958). (b) *Ibid., 3*, 34, Table 34, "Ionization Potentials." (c) Moore, *J. Opt. Soc. Am.* (1963), **53**, 886, on atomic spectra and configurations of elements with incomplete f subshells.
2. R. Latter, "Atomic Energy Levels . . . ," *Phys. Rev.* (1955), **99**, 510.
3. (a) L. Pauling, *The Nature of the Chemical Bond* (3rd ed., Ithaca, New York: Cornell University Press, 1960), Fig. 2–19, calculated electron energies vs. atomic number. (b) *Ibid.*, Sections 5–7 and 8–2, "The Electroneutrality Principle . . ." and Section 9–7, on bonding.* (c) *Ibid.*, Chapter 3, "The Partial Ionic Character of Covalent Bonds. . . ."
4. E. Clementi and D. L. Raimondi, "Atomic Screening Constants from SCF Functions," *J. Chem. Phys.* (1963), **38**, 2686, and earlier references therein.
5. M. Siegbahn, *Spektroskopie der Röntgenstrahlen* (2nd ed., Berlin: Springer, 1931), Table 176.
6. D. DeVault, *J. Chem. Ed.* (1944), **21**, 576, Fig. 1, "Accurate Energy Level Diagram of the Neutral Atoms."
7. H. E. White, *Introduction to Atomic Spectra* (New York: McGraw-Hill, 1934), Chapter 7, "Penetrating and Nonpenetrating Orbits . . . ," including Fig. 7–9.
8. W. Kauzmann, *Quantum Chemistry* (New York: Academic Press, 1957) pp. 324–332, "The Effect of Penetration . . ." and "Limitations on the Concept of an Orbital Energy."

* Concerning π-complexes of transition elements with unsaturated ligands.

9. M. G. Mayer, "Rare-Earth and Transuranic Elements," *Phys. Rev.* (1941), **60**, 184, on behavior of *f levels*.

10. R. N. Keller, "Energy Level Diagrams . . . ," *J. Chem. Ed.* (1962), **39**, 289.

11. (a) P. G. Dickens and J. W. Linnett, "Electron Correlation and Chemical Consequences," *Quart. Rev.* (1957), **11**, 291. (b) Linnett, "A Modification of the . . . Octet Rule," *J. Am. Chem. Soc.* (1961), **83**, 2643; numerous applications by Linnett appear in later articles.

12. C. K. Jørgensen, *Orbitals in Atoms and Molecules* (New York: Academic Press, 1962), Chapter 3, "Correlation Effects."

13. J. A. Pople, "The Molecular-Orbital and Equivalent-Orbital Approach . . . ," *Quart. Rev.* (1957), **11**, 273.

14. (a) M. J. Sienko and R. A. Plane, *Physical Inorganic Chemistry* (New York: Benjamin, 1963), Section 2–6, "Molecular Orbitals." (b) *Ibid.*, Section 2–7, "Three-Center Bonds"; also W. N. Lipscomb, *Boron Hydrides* (New York: Benjamin, 1963), Chapter 2.

15. (a) H. A. Bent, *Inorg. Chem.* (1963), **2**, 747, on bonding in N_2O_4. (b) Bent, ". . . Hybridization in Compounds of the First-Row Elements," *Chem. Rev.* (1961), **61**, 275.

16. C. A. Coulson, *J. Chem. Soc.* (1964), 1442, a review of bonding in xenon fluorides.

17. H. H. Hyman, also J. J. Kaufman, *J. Chem. Ed.* (1964), **41**, 178 and 183, both on bonding in noble-gas compounds.

18. R. E. Rundle, "The Implications of Some Recent Structures for Chemical Valence Theory," *Survey Prog. Chem.* (New York: Academic Press, 1963), **1**, 81, Section II, "The Rare Gas Rule . . ." and Section III B, on molecular orbitals in polyhalides, etc.

19. R. J. Gillespie, "The Valence-Shell Electron-Pair Repulsion Theory of Directed Valency," *J. Chem. Ed.* (1963), **40**, 295; see also M. C. Day and J. Selbin, *Theoretical Inorganic Chemistry* (New York: Reinhold, 1962), pp. 189–214, "Modern Stereochemical Theories" and related topics.

20. N. V. Sidgwick, *The Chemical Elements and Their Compounds* (London: Oxford, 1950), **1**, 547–548 on the "effective atomic number" and the inert-gas rule.

21. W. F. Griffith, *Quart. Rev.* (1962), **16**, 188, on CN⁻.*

22. (a) L. E. Orgel, *An Introduction to Transition-Metal Chemistry*

* Concerning π-complexes of transition elements with unsaturated ligands.

(London: Methuen, 1960), Section 9–7, "The inert-gas structure," including why planar complexes have 16-, not 18-electron structures. (b) *Ibid.*, Chapter 9, "The Lowest Valencies of the Transition Metals" and Chapter 10 on unsaturated hydrocarbons.*

23. E. W. Abel, *Quart. Rev.* (1963), **17**, 137, on CO.*
24. G. Wilkinson and A. F. Cotton, *Prog. Inorg. Chem.* (New York: Interscience, 1959), **1**, 1, on Cpd and arenes.*
25. R. S. Nyholm, "Electron Configuration and Structure of Transition-metal Complexes," *Proc. Chem. Soc.* (1961), p. 273.
26. C. A. Coulson, *Valence* (2nd ed., London: Oxford, 1961), Chapters IV, V, and VI on molecular-orbital and valence-bond theories and comparisons.
27. E. Cartmell and G. W. A. Fowles, *Valency and Molecular Structure* (2nd ed., London: Butterworths, 1961), Chapter 12 on chemical bonding in complex compounds.
28. E. O. Fischer and H. P. Fritz, *Adv. Inorg. Radiochem.* (New York: Academic Press, 1959), **1**, 55, on Cpd and arenes.*
29. R. G. Guy and B. L. Shaw, *Adv. Inorg. Radiochem.* (New York: Academic Press, 1962), **4**, 78, on olefins and acetylenes.*
30. G. E. Coates, *Organo-Metallic Compounds* (2nd ed., London: Methuen, 1960), pp. 237–249 on bonding.*
31. *Organometallic Chemistry,* ed. H. Zeiss (New York: Reinhold, 1960): J. W. Richardson, Chapter 1, on bonding*; P. L. Pauson, Chapter 7, on Cpd*; Zeiss, Chapter 8 on arenes.*
32. W. F. Little, *Survey Prog. Chem.* (New York: Academic Press, 1963), **1**, 133, on Cpd.*
33. J. Lewis, *Sci. Prog.* (1959), **47**, 206, on NO.*
34. L. Malatesta, *Prog. Inorg. Chem.* (New York: Interscience, 1959), **1**, 283, on isocyanides.*
35. E. O. Fischer and H. Werner, *Angew. Chem. in English* (1963), **2**, 80, on olefins.*
36. H. P. Fritz, *Adv. Organomet. Chem.* (New York: Academic Press, 1964), **1**, 239, on cyclo-C_nH_n.*
37. D. P. Craig and G. Doggett, "Theoretical Basis of the Rare-gas Rule," *J. Chem. Soc.* (1963), p. 4189 (found too late to discuss in text).
38. M. D. Rausch, *Can. J. Chem.* (1963), **41**, 1289, on Cpd.*

* Concerning π-complexes of transition elements with unsaturated ligands.

2

Atomic Radius

Chemical literature already contains numerous presentations of atomic radii against the background of the periodic table. These show the familiar contraction toward the right-hand side, but this contraction is often interrupted, unfortunately, by a mysteriously abrupt expansion at the noble gases. Labored "explanations" show that various misunderstandings have resulted either *in* this misconception or *from* it. A real but more gradual and uneven increase (toward the far right) in the historically important gram-atomic volume makes sense in terms of decreasing valence and the weakening of interatomic attractive forces averaged among all neighbors of a given atom in the crystal. Still, it would be quite a surprise to find, in such a series as Na, Mg, Al, Si, P, S, Cl, and Ar, that the atomic radius, defined reasonably, could increase (at argon) immediately *before* the establishment of a new outer shell of electrons and in spite of the continued increase of nuclear charge. Actually, this is quite a misleading impression due to the practice of comparing, in one table, the covalent or metallic radii of most elements with van der Waals or nonbonded radii of the noble gases.

2-1   IONIC AND VAN DER WAALS RADIUS

Crystal radii, for univalent and bivalent anions except hydride (for example, S^{2-}), are essentially identical with van der Waals radii (which are therefore not listed separately in Table 2–1) for the same elements in covalent compounds [for example, $(CH_3)_2S$]. This is expected because these covalent atoms, other than hydrogen, show to the outside world the same unshared electrons as do their anions, except in the direction of the covalent bond.

Table 2–1 gives crystal or van der Waals radii for various isoelectronic series.[1,2] With increasing nuclear charge, the radius decreases slowly until the noble gases are reached and then falls rapidly. This behavior can be considered to result from a combination of smoothly decreasing intrinsic radii together with the effect of electrostatic compressive forces (between ions), which are greatest for the most highly charged ions, whether positive or negative. Values for highly charged ions, very small cations, or large anions cannot be taken too seriously, however, since their bonding is relatively covalent. And when we speak of the *chemistry* of an ion such as S^{+6}, we will have in mind well known forms, typified by SO_4^{2-} in this example.

Proceeding down the columns from ns^2np^6 to $ns^2np^6nd^{10}$, where the $n + 1$ shell is still empty, we find a general decrease in size at constant charge. Compare Ca^{2+} and Zn^{2+}, for example. Where a new shell has been opened with only the two s electrons (for example, Ge^{2+}), the size may be slightly affected either way. The inclusion in a new shell of both s and p electrons (for example, Sr^{2+}) causes enough *increase* in size, however, to account for the over-all increase from top to bottom. The very large percentage increase between the first and second rows, most notable for the polyvalent cations, is partly responsible for the great chemical differences between **2sp** and **3sp** elements.

Pairs of horizontal series containing two ions of equal charge and nearly equal size (for example, Na^+ and Cu^+ or Ca^{2+} and Cd^{2+}) show clearly that the radii of the noble-gas type of ions are more sensitive to net charge than are the radii of the 18-electron type. This is reasonable because in series of the latter type the increase of nuclear charge is a smaller fraction of the total. The great chemical differences between Na^+ and Cu^+, having similar radii, and the chemical similarities between S^{6+} and Se^{6+} in the same series, having different radii, prove that charge and size do not completely determine properties. But S^{6+} and Se^{6+} have different types of subshells in the outer shell, as well as different radii. The similarity in their

Table 2-1 *Isoelectronic Series of Ionic and van der Waals or Nonbonded Radii*

Outer elect conf

$1s^2$
	H^-	He	Li^+	Be^{2+}	B^{3+}	C^{4+}	N^{5+}
	>1.5	1.2_8*	0.68	0.35	0.23	0.16	0.13
	1.2*						

$2s^2\,2p^6$
N	O^{2-}	F^-	Ne	Na^+	Mg^{2+}	Al^{3+}	Si^{4+}	P^{5+}	S^{6+}	Cl^{7+}
1.5*	1.40	1.36	1.3_9*	0.97	0.67	0.52	0.42	0.35	0.30	0.27

$2s^2\,2p^6\,3s^2$
P^{3+}	S^{4+}	Cl^{5+}
0.44	0.37	0.33

$3s^2\,3p^6$
P	S^{2-}	Cl^-	Ar	K^+	Ca^{2+}	Sc^{3+}	Ti^{4+}	V^{5+}	Cr^{6+}	Mn^{7+}
1.9*	1.84	1.81	1.7_1*	1.33	0.99	0.81	0.68	0.59	0.52	0.46

$3s^2\,3p^6\,3d^{10}$
Cu^+	Zn^{2+}	Ga^{3+}	Ge^{4+}	As^{5+}	Se^{6+}
0.96	0.74	0.62	0.53	0.46	0.42

$3s^2\,3p^6\,3d^{10}\,4s^2$
Ge^{2+}	As^{3+}	Se^{4+}	Br^{5+}
0.73	0.58	0.50	0.47

$4s^2\,4p^6$
As	Se^{2-}	Br^-	Kr	Rb^+	Sr^{2+}	Y^{3+}	Zr^{4+}	Nb^{5+}	Mo^{6+}	Tc^{7+}	Ru^{8+}
2.0*	1.98	1.95	1.8_0*	1.47	1.12	0.92	0.79	0.69	0.62	0.57	0.5

$4s^2\,4p^6\,4d^{10}$
Ag^+	Cd^{2+}	In^{3+}	Sn^{4+}	Sb^{5+}	Te^{6+}	I^{7+}
1.26	0.97	0.81	0.71	0.62	0.56	0.50

$4s^2\,4p^6\,4d^{10}\,5s^2$
Sn^{2+}	Sb^{3+}	Te^{4+}	I^{5+}
0.93	0.76	0.70	0.62

$4f^0\,5s^2\,5p^6$
Sb	Te^{2-}	I^-	Xe	Cs^+	Ba^{2+}	La^{3+}	Ce^{4+}
2.2*	2.21	2.16	2.0*	1.67	1.34	1.14	0.94

$4f^7\,5s^2\,5p^6$
Eu^{2+}	Gd^{3+}	Tb^{4+}
1.09	0.97	0.81

$4f^{14}\,5s^2\,5p^6$
Yb^{2+}	Lu^{3+}	Hf^{4+}	Ta^{5+}	W^{6+}	Re^{7+}	Os^{8+}
0.93	0.85	0.78	0.68	0.62	0.56	0.5

$5s^2\,5p^6\,5d^{10}$
Au^+	Hg^{2+}	Tl^{3+}	Pb^{4+}	Bi^{5+}
1.37	1.10	0.95	0.84	0.74

$5s^2\,5p^6\,5d^{10}\,6s^2$
Au^-	Tl^+	Pb^{2+}	Bi^{3+}
2.02	1.47	1.20	0.93

$5f^0\,6s^2\,6p^6$
Po^{2-}	At^-	Rn	Fr^+	Ra^{2+}	Ac^{3+}	Th^{4+}	Pa^{5+}	U^{6+}
2.3	2.2_5	2.2*	1.8	1.43	1.18	1.02	0.9	0.80

*van der Waals radii only. Some radii from miscellaneous sources.

chemistry, then, may result partly from a cancellation of the effects of these two differences. The chemical resemblance between S^{6+} and Te^{6+} is in some ways (such as stability to reduction though not coordination number) even greater. On the other hand, S^{2-} and Se^{2-}, with identical types of outer electron orbitals, are probably more alike chemically than S^{6+} and Se^{6+}. We notice also in this connection that the radii of the former pair differ by a much smaller percentage.

Having thus noted the importance of the d electrons in differentiating Na^+ and Cu^+, we might be surprised at the great similarity between the group Y^{3+}, Zr^{4+}, Nb^{5+}, Mo^{6+}, Tc^{7+}, and Ru^{8+} and the group Lu^{3+}, Hf^{4+}, Ta^{5+}, W^{6+}, Re^{7+}, and Os^{8+}. Zirconium and hafnium have been more difficult to separate than any other pair of elements. Molybdophosphates and tungstophosphates, but not chromophosphates, are well known. RuO_4 and OsO_4 are fairly stable, but FeO_4 does not exist. These two groups of ions do have nearly identical radii, but the heavier group comes just after the completion of an f subshell, while the lighter group has a noble-gas structure. The explanation is that the $4f$ electrons are not part of the exposed outer shell, whose principal quantum number in the heavy group is 5, whereas the d electrons—for example, in Cu^+—*are* exposed. We must note, however, that the $4f$ subshell, even though buried, has some effect on oxidation states where it is incomplete. In later chapters there is further discussion of cases where size and charge are dominant as well as of those where electronic configurational differences assert themselves.

We have not yet examined adequately why Hf^{4+}, for example, is no larger than Zr^{4+} although Zr^{4+} is definitely larger than Ti^{4+}. Table 2–2 shows the contraction associated, not with the addition of protons alone, as in the rows in Table 2–1, but even with the addition of protons plus an equal number of electrons (as long as new shells are not begun). The added protons are, of course, concentrated, but the electrons are dispersed, so we expect a net increase of attractive force on each electron and the resultant over-all contraction. The only surprising finding, then, is that the contraction is somewhat irregular, and even reversible, in the **d** series, where the so-called differentiating electrons are near the surface. Actually, there is some uncertainty of definition in these cases because most of the ions are not truly spherical. For example, the nine d electrons in Cu^{2+}

Table 2-2 *Ionic Radii in Isovalent Series*

Number of Outer d or f Electrons:

0	1	2	3	4	5	6	7	8	9	10	11	12	13	14
Ca^{2+} 0.99			V^{2+} 0.88		Mn^{2+} 0.80	Fe^{2+} 0.74	Co^{2+} 0.73	Ni^{2+} 0.69	Cu^{2+} 0.72	Zn^{2+} 0.74				
Sc^{3+} 0.81	Ti^{3+} 0.76	V^{3+} 0.74	Cr^{3+} 0.63	Mn^{3+} 0.66	Fe^{3+} 0.64	Co^{3+} 0.63				Ga^{3+} 0.62				
Zr^{4+} 0.79	Nb^{4+} 0.74	Mo^{4+} 0.69		Ru^{4+} 0.67		Pd^{4+} 0.69				Sn^{4+} 0.71				
Hf^{4+} 0.78		W^{4+} 0.70	Re^{4+} 0.72	Os^{4+} 0.69	Ir^{4+} 0.68	Pt^{4+} 0.65				Pb^{4+} 0.84				
La^{3+} 1.14	Ce^{3+} 1.07	Pr^{3+} 1.06	Nd^{3+} 1.04	Pm^{3+} 1.02	Sm^{3+} 1.00	Eu^{3+} 0.98	Gd^{3+} 0.97	Tb^{3+} 0.93	Dy^{3+} 0.92	Ho^{3+} 0.91	Er^{3+} 0.89	Tm^{3+} 0.87	Yb^{3+} 0.86	Lu^{3+} 0.85
Ac^{3+} 1.18			U^{3+} 1.12	Np^{3+} 1.10	Pu^{3+} 1.08	Am^{3+} 1.07								
Th^{4+} 1.02	Pa^{4+} 0.98	U^{4+} 0.97	Np^{4+} 0.95	Pu^{4+} 0.93	Am^{4+} 0.92									

can be assigned the detailed configuration $d_{xy}^2 d_{yz}^2 d_{zx}^2 d_{z^2}^2 d_{x^2-y^2}^1$. This is the same as the spherically symmetrical d^{10} configuration plus an electron vacancy in the $d_{x^2-y^2}$ orbital. The ion is therefore smaller along the x and y axes than along the z axis. In a few compounds, however, the Cu^{2+} is better described as having the vacancy in the d_{z^2} orbital. In any case, some of these effects are not yet well understood. The ions in the f series have the differentiating electrons well buried and so remain essentially spherical.

In any case, between zirconium and hafnium there are the same contractions as between titanium and zirconium, plus the f series (or so-called lanthanide) contraction. Together these contractions happen to balance the expansion due to placement of 8 electrons into a completely new shell. In other words, only one new electron shell was established while 32 protons, rather than 18 or 8 as before, were added to the nucleus.

2-2 COVALENT AND METALLIC RADIUS

The contraction of atomic radius with increasing atomic number in each period of the periodic table can be seen in a different way in Fig. 2–1. Experimental values of "single-bond" metallic and covalent radii are available for almost every element.[2] At the beginning of each period there is a large contraction as the number of valence electrons increases. Clearly these valence electrons participate in metallic bonding and pull the atoms together. In fact these atoms (at the extreme left) can be regarded as having ionized, even in the metal, with the loss of all the valence electrons to the surrounding electron "sea." In further support of this, the extent of contraction is observed to be comparable to that noted in Table 2–1 for the cations with inert-gas structures. The corresponding metallic radii in Fig. 2–1 are all larger by roughly the same amount, 0.7 Å. On the basis of these radii and other properties (see next paragraph) metallic valences can be assigned, as discussed by Pauling,[2] equal to the maximum ordinary valences in the case of these easily oxidizable metals. Such valences approximate the number of electrons apparently pooled with the other atoms in the crystal.

Following the regions of abrupt contraction are regions of gradual contraction, for example, from approximately chro-

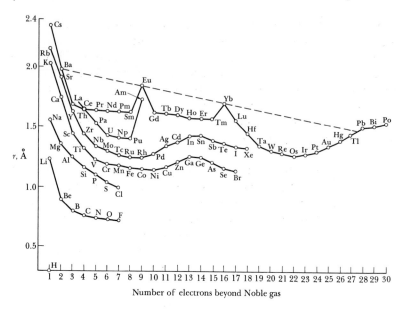

Fig. 2–1. Metallic and covalent radii.

mium to nickel or from lanthanum to lutetium. Here the degree of contraction is similar to that seen in Table 2–2 for isovalent ions. The conclusion is that elements in each of these regions have achieved a nearly constant metallic valence. This conclusion is supported by properties such as hardness, melting point, magnetic moment, and so on. An estimated metallic valence of 6 for the **3d** metals in this region agrees with the ordinary maximum valence for chromium, although certainly not for the others. The **4d** and **5d** metals appear to reach a higher metallic valence, in agreement with their tendency toward higher oxidation states in compounds. Apparent metallic valences of 3 for most of the rare earths and of 6 for the uranium series are the same as the ordinary maximum valence states for most of these. The valences for europium and ytterbium are evidently 2 in the metal as they sometimes are in compounds. The radii for these elements are practically on a straight line between barium and lead, which are also ordinarily bivalent. The bivalence of europium and ytterbium is evidently stabilized by the attainment of a 4f subshell that is exactly either half full or full, respectively, without the loss of a third electron.

The metals farther to the right show a gradual increase in radius. From this we conclude that the metallic valences decrease smoothly while the ordinary valences, although also smaller in these regions, are less uniform in trend. The falling energy of the d electrons here, as seen in Fig. 1–1, makes them less available for sharing with their neighbors.

The decreases in radii of nonmetals, at the extreme right, still have to be considered. Covalences for these elements are well known, decreasing to the value of one in the halogens. We may wonder whether a drop in valence or in holding power for neighboring atoms should not lead to expansion of interatomic distances, as in the metals. It does, in fact, if the distance is taken to be the average for all the atoms in contact with a given atom in the solid state of the element, as is done with metals. The difference is that in a metal there are often 8 to 12 atoms in contact at about the same distance. (Note that there are no unshared electrons to keep some of the neighbors at a greater distance.) In a nonmetal a few atoms are held closer, thus defining the covalent radii used here, while the others are at greater distances, corresponding to weak van der Waals forces. Gram-atomic volumes, reflecting the net result, do increase (unevenly) toward the next noble gas.

The vertical trends in metallic and covalent radii can mostly be interpreted by the principles used in the preceding section. The main exception, already implied but not explained, is that the early 5f elements have larger metallic valences and smaller metallic radii than the 4f, although this merely carries further a trend seen among the d elements. Certainly the f series (lanthanide) and d series contractions explain part of the vertical relationship in radii. An additional shrinkage of the heavier atoms is related to their larger valences. The latter, in turn, are probably caused mainly by smaller ionization energies in the *last* stages of ionization, even if not in the *first* ones. These energies, however, are not well known experimentally or fully predictable theoretically.

REFERENCES

1. L. H. Ahrens, "Use of Ionization Potentials. I. Ionic Radii . . . ," *Geochim. Cosmochim. Acta* (1952), **2**, 155.
2. L. Pauling, *The Nature of the Chemical Bond* (3rd ed., Ithaca, New York: Cornell University Press, 1960), Section 13–2, ionic radii; Sections 7–11, 11–2 to 11–4, and 11–8, metallic valence and radii; Chapter 7, "Interatomic Distances . . ."
3. K. H. Stern and E. S. Amis, "Ionic Size," *Chem. Rev.* (1959), **59**, 1.
4. L. E. Sutton, ed., *Tables of Interatomic Distance and Configuration in Molecules and Ions. Spec. Pub. 11* (London: The Chemical Society, 1958).
5. G. Derflinger and O. E. Polansky, "Über den Zusammenhang von Kovalenzradien und Electronegativitäten," *Theor. Chim. Acta* (1963), **1**, 316.

3

Ionization Energy, Electron Affinity, and Electronegativity

In Section 1–2 we examined the influence of atomic number on the energies of the several kinds of orbitals. These energies were defined by reference to the gain or loss of an electron, but the states involved were either averages of the spectroscopic states for each electron configuration or estimated states in which complications would not obscure the main effects of penetration and increased nuclear charge.

3-1 IONIZATION ENERGY AND ELECTRON AFFINITY

The present subject is different in several ways. We frequently want to know the actual ionization energies (often called ionization potentials), as measured from the *highest* filled levels in the ground states of atoms or ions. (See Reference 1 and Chapter 1, Reference 1b.) The trends we find include the trends in orbital energies, but also discontinuities due to successively half-filling or filling the various subshells. We can conveniently treat electron affinities as ordinary ionization energies, but involving negative ions. (See Fig. 3–1.) Most of these affinities,[2-3] however, are rather rough estimates.

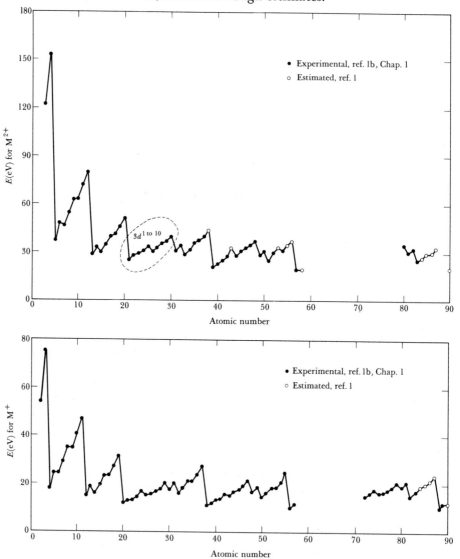

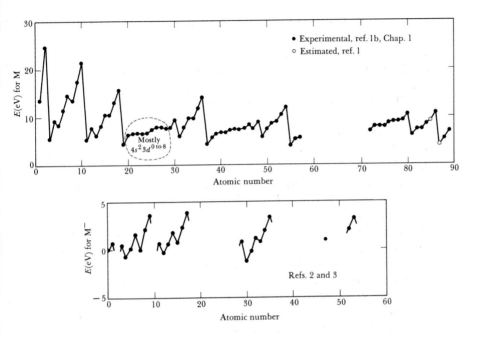

Fig. 3–1. Ionization energies of atoms with various charges, or electron affinities of atoms with an additional positive charge. Circles are extrapolations from Reference 1.

To compare trends in Section 1–2 and here, it is necessary to note that the smaller energies are toward the top in the former case and toward the bottom in Fig. 3–1. These follow the established conventions for diagrams of both the orbital energy levels and the ionization energies.

It is easy to see that the drops or breaks in the curves come whenever a new subshell or the second half of one is started. Examples would include $_3$Li (one $2s$ electron), $_{17}$Cl$^+$ (a half-full $3p$ subshell plus a fourth $3p$ electron), $_{39}$Y^{2+} (one $4d$ electron), and so on. Between these breaks, the increases of energy represent the direct effect of increasing nuclear charge acting on the same subshell, with only partial screening by the other electrons added. The values for neutral atoms of the **d** elements show irregularities associated with the near equality in energies of the s and d electrons. Some of these irregularities can be interpreted with the help of Fig. 1–2. The values for **f** elements are not well known, but should also show complications. Polyvalent ions, on the other hand, have more straightforward patterns when d electrons are to be ionized (as in the neighborhood of $_{25}Mn^{2+}$); as we saw earlier, the s and d energies are well separated in these cases. For most highly charged ions, information is not available.

To illustrate the main trends in the columns of the periodic table, we can choose the example of $_7N^+$, $_{15}P^+$, $_{33}As^+$, $_{51}Sb^+$, and $_{83}Bi^+$. We see in Fig. 3–1 that the larger atoms or ions of such a family generally have the smaller ionization energies. This effect is seen to be greater, the larger the charge. For simple electrostatic reasons, of course, we would expect a large charge on a small ion to hold electrons strongly.

The smallness of the fluorine electron affinity (3.5 eV) compared to the chlorine value (3.7 eV) has sometimes been discussed by pointing out that our estimates are based squarely on a Born-Haber cycle which includes the now undisputed low energy of atomization (dissociation) for F_2. More relevantly for our attempts at explanation, we can say that the lightest atoms are not only the smallest (favoring large electron affinities because of the short distances between electrons and nuclei) but also those with the least nuclear charge (favoring small electron affinities). The net result is a balance whose outcome could not have been predicted qualitatively, although size turns out to be dominant in the analogous case of ionization energies.

Single ionization energies for O^{2-}, S^{2-}, and Se^{2-} (not plotted) are roughly -5 eV, -1 eV, and -2 eV, respectively. The minus sign reflects the mutual repulsion of the two negative charges. This is greatest for the small oxygen atom although an allowance for size would still leave an alternation here, as in some other properties of these elements and as we just saw for the halogens. Ionization energies for doubly negative ions without noble-gas structures would, of course, be even more negative. The chemical stability of these p4-group ions in compounds results, then, from the *relative* stability of the ions themselves plus large heats of hydration, lattice formation, and other interactions with the double negative charge.

Ahrens (Chapter 2, Reference 1) studied regularities in ionization energies, including the dependence on radius. On a log-log plot, excellent straight lines are obtained for the electron affinities of the alkali and alkaline-earth ions, excluding Li^+ and Be^{2+}, but not for other isovalent series. The **1sp** ions have only

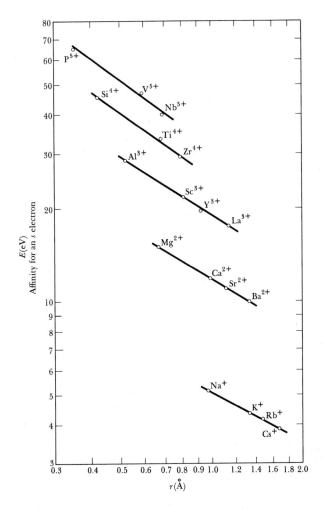

Fig. 3–2. Affinities of noble-gas type ions for an *s* electron, versus radius.

two outer electrons, while all the others have eight; therefore, the (downward) deviations of the smallest ions make sense. For the series with larger charges we can also find excellent linearity (Fig. 3–2) by comparing only ionization energies from ions with the one valence electron in the same state, that is, the lowest available *s* orbital. The **s1** and **s2** elements normally have their electrons in *s* orbitals, and so do Al^{2+}, Si^{3+}, and so on. But Sc^{2+}, as is typical of the transition ions, has a d electron in the ground state. Excitation from this $3d$ level to the lowest $4s$ level requires 3.16 eV in this example, thus reducing the normal ionization energy from 24.75 eV to an "s" ionization energy of 21.59 eV, as used in our Fig. 3–2. The slopes of the lines correspond neither to a constant nor to an integral power of the radius, although Ahrens' plots were closer to a second power. The present graph will be needed in Section 4–2.

Beryllium, magnesium, and zinc have negative electron affinities associated with complete subshells. For atoms with complete shells or subshells we might have expected electron affinities of zero, and negative values may seem surprising at first. Let us consider the quantum-mechanical problem of confining an electron to a cubic box the size of an atom. The reader should recall that the energy is $(n_x{}^2 + n_y{}^2 + n_z{}^2)h^2/8ml^2$. If we put the electron into an energy level similar to the $4p$ orbital on zinc, it would have altogether five nodes (other than the borders) in one direction and quantum numbers of 6, 1, and 1 for n_x, n_y and n_z. With a length l of 2.4 Å, equal to the diameter of the zinc atom, we arrive at an energy 200 eV higher than that of the free electron! This is a very rough picture but it certainly shows the importance of confinement operating against the attraction of the central nucleus.

Note that more energy is absorbed in removing electrons even from alkali metals than is returned in adding electrons even to halogen atoms. At close range the halogen atom has the greater attraction for the electron but the positive metal ion exerts some attraction even at moderate distances. The stability of ionic solids depends, of course, on the nearness of the oppositely charged ions to each other.

Entropies of ionization of monatomic gaseous atoms are negligible (and therefore not presented here) since the initial and final atoms or ions are both simple and have similar (translational) degrees of freedom.

3-2 ATOMIC AND ORBITAL ELECTRONEGATIVITY

The concept of electronegativity (ability of an atom to attract electrons within a molecule) has become mired in controversy, but it is still useful, even almost indispensable. It is increasingly agreed that we need to use different values for the

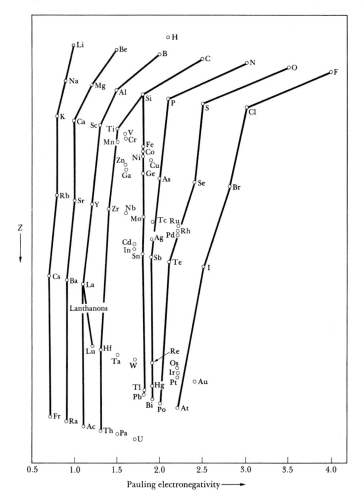

Fig. 3–3. Pauling's electronegativities.

various bonding orbitals of a given atom, although single-valued or atomic electronegativities will continue to be applied, especially where other data are inadequate. Of course, the concept can also lose usefulness by becoming *too* flexible.

For discussion of the many definitions proposed, and for numerous additional references, the reader is referred to other sources.[2b, 4-14] Here we compare only three sets of single-valued and one set of orbital electronegativities.

Table 3-1 *"Electrostatic" Electronegativities*[6,7]

H (2.1)																
Li 0.97	Be 1.47											B 2.01	C 2.50	N 3.07	O 3.50	F 4.10
Na 1.01	Mg 1.23											Al 1.47	Si 1.74	P 2.06	S 2.44	Cl 2.83
K 0.91	Ca 1.04	Sc 1.20	Ti 1.32	V 1.45	Cr 1.56	Mn 1.60	Fe 1.64	Co 1.70	Ni 1.75	Cu 1.75	Zn 1.66	Ga 1.82	Ge 2.02	As 2.20	Se 2.48	Br 2.74
Rb 0.89	Sr 0.99	Y 1.11	Zr 1.22	Nb 1.23	Mo 1.30	Tc 1.36	Ru 1.42	Rh 1.45	Pd 1.35	Ag 1.42	Cd 1.46	In 1.49	Sn 1.72	Sb 1.82	Te 2.01	I 2.21
Cs 0.86	Ba 0.97	La 1.08 / Lu 1.14	Hf 1.23	Ta 1.33	W 1.40	Re 1.46	Os 1.52	Ir 1.55	Pt 1.44	Au 1.42	Hg 1.44	Tl 1.44	Pb 1.55	Bi 1.67	Po 1.76	At 1.90
Fr 0.86	Ra 0.97	Ac 1.00														

Lanthanides: La 1.08, Ce 1.08, Pr 1.07, Nd 1.07, Pm 1.07, Sm 1.07, Eu 1.01, Gd 1.11, Tb 1.10, Dy 1.10, Ho 1.10, Er 1.11, Tm 1.11, Yb 1.06, Lu 1.14

Actinides: Ac 1.00, Th 1.11, Pa 1.14, U 1.22, Np 1.22, Pu 1.22, Am 1.22(1.2) →, Cm, Bk, Cf, Es, Fm, Md, No, Lw

Figure 3–3 shows the periodic variations in Pauling's well-known assignments, while Table 3–1 presents those of Little and Jones, based on Allred and Rochow's definition and partial list. The latter values are chosen because of their good theoretical foundation, their completeness, and the fact that they bring out significant alternations in the columns of **p** elements. These electronegativities are calculated from the electrostatic force of attraction on an electron in an atom at the distance of the covalent radius from the nucleus. The equation is

$$x = .359(Z_{eff}/r^2) + .744$$

where x is the electronegativity, Z_{eff} is the effective nuclear charge, r is the covalent radius, and the constants merely serve to relate the attractive force to the range of electronegativities originally chosen by Pauling. In contrast, several scales, including Pauling's, are related to energy quantities such as heats of reaction. For hydrogen, the Pauling result is adopted by Little and Jones because the covalent radius in this case is not at all constant.

Because it has now become fairly common in more elementary courses to point out certain periodic trends in electronegativity, the discussion here will not include all aspects. The alternations in **p** columns (according to some measures) have already been referred to. Many chemical and physical facts suggest such alternations and even further ones not evident in any complete and consistent scale of electronegativity. Sanderson's values, in Fig. 3–4, bring out this feature more than most. These are based on comparison of atomic electron densities (but calculated from the *covalent* radius) with noble-gas electron densities (calculated using radii interpolated from isoelectronic *ions*). Even this scale shows chlorine intermediate between fluorine and bromine, and so does not explain, for example, the relative stability of ClO_4^- and the nonexistence of FO_4^- and BrO_4^-. On the other hand, the nonalternating progression from fluorine to iodine in all scales does correspond to the trend in ease of oxidation of the simple halide ions. This brings out the fact that no single-valued measure of the ability to attract electrons within molecules can correlate perfectly with all observations affected by the tendency to hold electrons.

The noble gases point up certain difficulties with some applications of the whole concept. If these elements have high

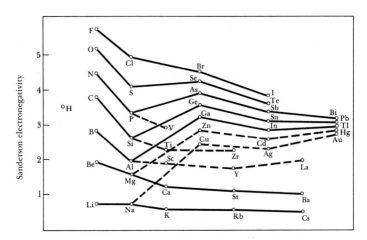

Fig. 3–4. Alternations in Sanderson's electronegativities.

electronegativities, they ought to react vigorously with the alkali metals, but they do not. But if they have medium or low electronegativities, they should combine violently with F_2 (because no protective surface coating can form as with certain metals), whereas they are actually either inert or reactive only at higher temperatures and pressures. The problem, of course, is that these elements hold their own electrons strongly, but additional ones not at all. This suggests using the separate ionization potential and electron affinity rather than electronegativity, which, by Mulliken's definition, is the average of the other two anyway. Another small difficulty in Sanderson's scale is that it assigns values of 1 to all the noble gases, not allowing for any variation within the group.

Mulliken's definition is the basis of the more flexible orbital electronegativities calculated by Hinze and Jaffé. In their method, various "valence states" are constructed from weighted averages of spectroscopic states. (An example of a valence state not found in spectroscopy would be the sp^3 hybrid, constructed from s and p states.) Semi-empirical calculations are then made of ionization potentials and electron affinities for these valence states. The Mulliken electronegativity is next obtained and transformed to the Pauling type by the equation $x_p = .336(x_M - .615)$. The results in Tables 3–2, 3–3 and 3–4 are selected from those most relevant in ordinary chemistry. The values for transition

Table 3-2 Valence–State Ionization Energies, I_v *

s1	s2	p1	p2	p3	p4	p5
H s 13.60						
Li s 5.39	Be $didi$ 8.58	B $trtrtr$ 11.29	C $tetete$ 14.61 $trtrtr\,\pi$ 15.62 *11.16* $didi\,\pi\pi$ 17.42 *11.19*	N s^2ppp 13.94 $te^2tetete$ 18.93 $tr^2trtr\,\pi$ 20.60 *14.12* $di^2di\,\pi\pi$ 23.91 *14.18*	O s^2p^2pp 17.28 te^2te^2tete 24.39 $tr^2tr^2tr\,\pi$ 26.65 *17.70*	F $s^2p^2p^2p$ 20.86
Na s 5.14	Mg $didi$ 7.10	Al $trtrtr$ 8.83	Si $tetete$ 11.82	P s^2ppp 10.73 $te^2tetete$ 14.57	S s^2p^2pp 12.39 te^2te^2tete 15.50 $tr^2tr^2tr\,\pi$ 16.33 *12.70*	Cl $s^2p^2p^2p$ 15.03
K s 4.34	Ca $didi$ 5.76	Ga $trtrtr$ 9.76	Ge $tetete$ 11.48	As s^2ppp 9.36 $te^2tetete$ 12.80	Se s^2p^2pp 11.68 te^2te^2tete 15.29 $tr^2tr^2tr\,\pi$ 15.68 *12.59*	Br $s^2p^2p^2p$ 13.10
Rb s 4.18	Sr $didi$ 5.34	In $trtrtr$ 8.68	Sn $tetete$ 10.40	Sb s^2ppp 8.75 $te^2tetete$ 13.16	Te s^2p^2pp 11.04 te^2te^2tete 15.11 $tr^2tr^2tr\,\pi$ 15.36 *12.29*	I $s^2p^2p^2p$ 12.67

*Italicized numbers for π–bonding; others for σ–bonding.

Table 3–3 Valence–State Electron Affinities, E_v *

s1	s2	p1	p2	p3	p4	p5
H s 0.75						
Li s 0.82	Be didi 0.99	B trtrtr 1.38	C tetetete 1.34 trtrtr π 1.95 0.03 didi ππ 3.34 0.10	N 0.84 s² ppp te² tetete 4.15 tr² trtr π 5.14 1.78 di² di ππ 7.45 1.66	O 2.01 s² p² pp te² te² tete 6.11 tr² tr² tr π 7.49 2.47	F 3.50 s² p² p² p
Na s 0.47	Mg didi 1.08	Al trtrtr 2.11	Si tetetete 2.78	P 1.42 s² ppp te² tetete 3.24	S 2.38 s² p² pp te² te² tete 4.77 tr² tr² tr π 5.43 2.76	Cl 3.73 s² p² p² p
K s 1.46	Ca didi 1.02	Ga trtrtr 2.28	Ge tetetete 4.66	As 1.33 s² ppp te² tetete 3.81	Se 2.52 s² p² pp te² te² tete 4.24 tr² tr² tr π 5.14 2.37	Br 3.70 s² p² p² p
Rb s 0.0	Sr didi 0.93	In trtrtr 1.89	Sn tetetete 5.39	Sb 1.18 s² ppp te² tetete 3.79	Te 2.58 s² p² pp te² te² tete 4.20 tr² tr² tr π 4.57 2.70	I 3.52 s² p² p² p

*Italicized numbers for π–bonding; others for σ–bonding.

Table 3–4   Valence-State Electronegativities, Pauling Scale, x_P*

| | | | | H | | |
| | | | | s 2.21 | | |

s1	s2	p1	p2	p3	p4	p5
Li	Be *didi* 1.40	B *trtrtr* 1.93	C *tetetete* 2.48 *trtrtr* π 2.75 *1.68* *didi* ππ 3.29 *1.69*	N s^2ppp 2.28 $te^2tetete$ 3.68 tr^2trtr π 4.13 *2.47* di^2di ππ 5.07 *2.46*	O s^2p^2pp 3.04 te^2te^2tete 4.93 tr^2tr^2tr π 5.54 *3.19*	F $s^2p^2p^2p$ 3.90
s 0.84						
Na	Mg *didi* 1.17	Al *trtrtr* 1.64	Si *tetetete* 2.25	P s^2ppp 1.84 $te^2tetete$ 2.79	S s^2p^2pp 2.28 te^2te^2tete 3.21 tr^2tr^2tr π 3.46 *2.40*	Cl $s^2p^2p^2p$ 2.95
s 0.74						
K	Ca *didi* 0.93	Ga *trtrtr* 1.82	Ge *tetetete* 2.50	As s^2ppp 1.59 $te^2tetete$ 2.58	Se s^2p^2pp 2.18 te^2te^2tete 3.07 tr^2tr^2tr π 3.29 *2.31*	Br $s^2p^2p^2p$ 2.62
s 0.77						
Rb	Sr *didi* 0.85	In *trtrtr* 1.57	Sn *tetetete* 2.44	Sb s^2ppp 1.46 $te^2tetete$ 2.64	Te s^2p^2pp 2.08 te^2te^2tete 3.04 tr^2tr^2tr π 3.17 *2.31*	I $s^2p^2p^2p$ 2.52
s 0.50						

*Italicized numbers for π–bonding; others for σ–bonding.

55

elements (not given here) are based on less reliable data and they seem considerably less appropriate for ordinary chemistry.

To understand the symbols in the table we can use the example of nitrogen. The first state listed has a full outer s orbital plus one electron in each p orbital. Because the electronegativity is based on both I_v and E_v (ionization energies and electron affinities, in electron volts, calculated for the various valence states constructed) and because a full orbital has no meaningful E_v, only the values for the p orbitals in this configuration are needed and listed. In bonding, these would ordinarily form σ bonds. The same is true for the tetrahedral orbitals (sp^3 hybrid, designated te) given next. On the other hand, if we use trigonal (sp^2 or tr) or digonal (sp or di) hybrid orbitals, one or two of the valence electrons will go into p-π valence states. In these cases separate values are calculated for σ and π bonding.

The results show the usual increase of electronegativity toward the right side of a row and a general decrease from top to bottom but with some alternations. In addition, we now see that π-bonding orbitals are less electronegative than σ and it can be found that electronegativity, but not I_v or E_v, increases linearly with increasing s character, going down the list for each element. In the example of nitrogen the four successive σ bonds have 0, $\frac{1}{4}$, $\frac{1}{3}$, and $\frac{1}{2}$ s character, respectively. It is interesting to see how constant the π values, always related to pure p orbitals, are for each element.

The numerical values are comparable to those of other authors in the case of the s1, s2, p1, p2, and p5 elements. Here also the valence states correspond rather clearly to the ones found in ordinary substances. On the other hand, compounds like NH_3 and H_2O have sometimes been described as having p valence orbitals with bond angles enlarged by internuclear repulsion, and sometimes as having tetrahedral orbitals with angles reduced by repulsions between shared and unshared electron pairs. So it is not too surprising that the various atomic electronegativities are intermediate between the corresponding orbital values.

The orbital electronegativities have also been extended rather elegantly by Hinze, Whitehead, and Jaffé to empty and full orbitals by using a definition equivalent to the Mulliken one for the ordinary case but of more general applicability.[9-10] Very briefly, $x_n \equiv \partial E_n / \partial E_n$ where E_n is the energy as a quadratic function of the degree n to which the orbital is filled, n varying continuously from 0 to 2. From $E_0 \equiv 0$, $E_1 = I_v$, and $E_2 = I_v + E_v$, it is fairly easy to get the result

$$x_n = n(E_v - I_v) + (3/2)I_v - (1/2)E_v.$$

This reduces to Mulliken's $(1/2)(I_v + E_v)$ for an ordinary singly occupied valence orbital, $n = 1$. There is not space here for the further applications of this interesting idea. This approach gives values for, say, the nitrogen configurations te^2te^2tete and te^2te^0tete, and another paper[10] gives values for various states in certain unipositive ions, such as $tetetete$ in gaseous N^+.

REFERENCES

1. W. Finkelnburg and W. Humbach, "Ionisierungsenergien von Atomen und Atomionen," *Naturwiss.* (1955), **42**, 35, including values extrapolated using screening constants.
2. (a) H. O. Pritchard, *Chem. Rev.* (1953), **52**, 529, on electron affinities. (b) Pritchard and H. A. Skinner, "The Concept of Electronegativity," *Chem. Rev.* (1955), **55**, 745, including p. 781, appendix, "Electron Affinities of Atoms."
3. D. D. Cubicciotti, Jr., *J. Chem. Phys.* (1959), **31**, 1646; (1960), **33**, 1579: on electron affinities of the halogens.
4. W. Gordy and W. J. O. Thomas, "Electronegativities . . . ," *J. Chem. Phys.* (1956), **24**, 439.
5. L. Pauling, *The Nature of the Chemical Bond* (3rd ed., Ithaca, New York: Cornell, 1960), Sections 3–6 through 3–10 on electronegativity.
6. A. L. Allred and E. G. Rochow, "A Scale of Electronegativity Based on Electrostatic Force," *J. Inorg. Nuc. Chem.* (1958), **5**, 264; *ibid.* (1958), **5**, 269, and (1961), **20**, 167, on **p2** elements (carbon, etc.); Allred and A. L. Hensly, *J. Inorg. Nuc. Chem.* (1961), **17**, 43, on **p3** elements; Allred, "Electronegativity Values from Thermochemical Data," *J. Inorg. Nuc. Chem.* (1961), **17**, 215.
7. E. J. Little and M. M. Jones, "A Complete Table of Electronegativities," *J. Chem. Ed.* (1960), **37**, 231.
8. R. T. Sanderson, *Chemical Periodicity* (New York: Reinhold, 1960), pp. 26–44, on "stability ratios" as a measure of electronegativity; Sanderson, "An Explanation of Chemical Variations within Periodic Major Groups," *J. Am. Chem. Soc.* (1952), **74**, 4792; Sanderson, "Alternations in electronegativity and the Pritchard and Skinner review," *J. Inorg. Nuc. Chem.* (1958), **7**, 157.

9. R. P. Iczkowski and J. L. Margrave, "Electronegativity," *J. Am. Chem. Soc.* (1961), **83**, 3547, defined as —dE/dN.

10. J. Hinze and H. H. Jaffé, "Orbital Electronegativities of Neutral Atoms," *J. Am. Chem. Soc.* (1962), **84**, 540; ". . . of the Neutral Atoms of the Periods Three A and Four A and of Positive Ions of Periods One and Two," *J. Phys. Chem.* (1963), **67**, 1501; ". . . of the Transition Metals," *Can. J. Chem.* (1963), **41**, 1515; with M. A. Whitehead, "Bond and Orbital Electronegativity," *J. Am. Chem. Soc.* (1963), **85**, 148. But see comment on last paper by H. O. Pritchard, "Equalization of Electronegativity," *J. Am. Chem. Soc.* (1963), **85**, 1876.

11. R. E. Rundle, *J. Am. Chem. Soc.* (1963), **85**, 112, includes electronegativities for the noble gases.

12. I. R. Beattie, "The Acceptor Properties of Quadripositive (Si, Ge, Sn, Pb)," *Quart. Rev.* (1963), **17**, 382, opposing an alternation in electronegativities.

13. V. P. Spiridonov and V. M. Tatevski, *Zhur. fiz. Khim.* (1963), **37**, 2174, one in a series attacking the concept of electronegativity; p. 2178, English summary.

14. C. K. Jørgensen, *Orbitals in Atoms and Molecules* (New York: Academic Press, 1962), Chapter 7, "Electronegativity and Chemical Bonding," including "optical electronegativity."

15. F. A. Cotton and G. Wilkinson, *Advanced Inorganic Chemistry* (New York: Wiley, 1962), Section 3–4, "Promotion Energies and Valence States."

16. J. K. Wilmshurst, *J. Chem. Phys.* (1957), **27**, 1129; (1958), **28**, 733, on calculation of group electronegativities.

17. D. H. McDaniel and A. Yingst, "The Use of Basicity and Oxidative Coupling Potential to Obtain Group Electronegativity," *J. Am. Chem. Soc.* (1964), **86**, 1334.

18. H. Ebinghaus, *Z. Naturforsch.* (1964), **19a**, 727, on electron affinities of the alkali metals.

19. R. J. S. Crossley, "Glockler's Equation for Ionization Potential and Electron Affinity," *Proc. Phys. Soc.* (1964), **83**, 375.

4

Polarization and Some
Thermodynamic Properties

The concept of polarization and a resultant partial covalency in bonding has been used both qualitatively and quantitatively to explain a wide variety of observations,[1-4] for example, the great difference in solubilities of AgI and KI, whose cations have nearly the same size. In the first two sections of this chapter, the periodicities of polarization properties will be examined. In the third section, a new and still empirical but quite general relationship between molecular polarizability and boiling point will be presented.* After the treatment of boiling points and some observations on intermolecular forces, the periodicity of interatomic forces will be noted, as shown by the thermodynamics of dissociation of elements into atoms. Some of the same principles will be applied to more complicated situations in Chapter 8.

* The author wishes to acknowledge gratefully that the main parts of this work were done at Bethel College with support from the Research Corporation and during a summer at the University of Utah.

4-1 POLARIZABILITY

A useful way to think of polarizability is that it represents the ease with which excited states can be mixed or hybridized with the ground state to produce or change polarity. Thus, s and p orbitals are both centered on the nucleus but an electron in a hybrid of the two will be found more on one side, where the wave functions are of the same sign, than on the other, where they partly cancel. This mixing and polarization in an electric field will be more extensive as the energy requirement is less for giving the orbital some of the character of the upper energy level, that is, as the energy separation between the levels is smaller. If the energy levels are close together, either the occupied ground state cannot be very low or the normally empty excited state cannot be very high. High polarizability therefore implies some ease of either losing or gaining an electron. The converse is not necessarily true, partly because, even in the case of really large electron affinities due to net positive charge, the net charge usually increases the *differences* in the energies, as well as their absolute values.

Since light is a source of varying electric fields, optical refraction experiments can be used to determine polarizabilities. (The fact that this cannot be done, however, for polarizing strengths [polarizing powers] partly accounts for the much less numerous data on the latter property.) The large values expected for large oxidizable negative ions, those having many outer mobile electrons, are evident in the lists of both cations and anions given elsewhere.[5] In the present work, we have more need of the polarizabilities or refractivities of neutral atoms.

Table 4–1 gives Batsanov's values[6] of gram-atomic refractivity R. These are related to polarizabilities α by $R = 4\pi\alpha N/3$, where N is Avogadro's number. The values for nonmetals are based directly on measurements of the index of refraction n of the elements, using the Lorenz-Lorentz formula

$$R = \frac{n^2 - 1}{n^2 + 2} V,$$

where V is the volume of one gram-atomic weight. V and n vary with conditions but R is nearly constant.

The optical behavior of metals is such that they can be

Table 4-1 *Atomic Refractivities (cc/gram-atom)*

H	He
1.02	0.50

H	He
1.02	0.50

Li	Be											B	C	N	O	F	Ne
12.6	4.8											3.5	2.08	2.20	1.99	1.60	0.95

Na	Mg											Al	Si	P	S	Cl	Ar
22.8	13.8											9.9	9.06	8.6	7.6	5.71	4.00

K	Ca	Sc	Ti	V	Cr	Mn	Fe	Co	Ni	Cu	Zn	Ga	Ge	As	Se	Br	Kr
43.4	25.6	15.	10.7	8.2	7.2	7.3	7.0_5	6.6	6.5_5	7.0_5	8.9	11.6	11.08	10.3	10.8	8.09	6.04

Rb	Sr	Y	Zr	Nb	Mo	Tc	Ru	Rh	Pd	Ag	Cd	In	Sn	Sb	Te	I	Xe
53.1	33.2	20.2	13.9	10.8_5	9.4	(8.4)	8.1	8.2	8.8	10.1	12.7	15.3	16.0	18.1	14.4	14.08	9.90

Cs	Ba	Lu	Hf	Ta	W	Re	Os	Ir	Pt	Au	Hg	Tl	Pb	Bi	Po	At	Rn
65.9	37.3	17.9	13.4	10.8_5	9.5	8.8	8.4	8.5	9.0	10.1	13.8	16.9	17.9	21.0			

Fr	Ra

Lw

La	Ce	Pr	Nd	Pm	Sm	Eu	Gd	Tb	Dy	Ho	Er	Tm	Yb
22.1	20.6	20.7	20.6		21.7	29.0	19.7	19.1	19.0	18.8	18.2	18.1	24.7

Ac	Th	Pa	U	Np	Pu	Am	Cm	Bk	Cf	Es	Fm	Md
	19.8	15.0	12.5	11.6		20.8						

treated as having large complex values of n. In the limit for large n (complex or real) we have $R = V$. Therefore, the values for the metals, mostly in the absence of direct measurements, are taken by Batsanov to be simply the gram-atomic volumes. Another argument for this is the assumption that R represents the "true" molar volume of a substance, not counting the empty and therefore nonrefractive spaces between the atoms. Because metals can be considered as positive ions immersed in a sea of electrons, there are no empty spaces in them.

The additivity of refractivities for elements in various compounds (with corrections for double bonds and other structural features) used to be employed more often, before the coming of modern instrumentation, to decide structural questions in organic chemistry.

The periodicities of refractivity are mostly as expected. The heavier atoms, having more electrons and more mobile outer ones, are larger and more refractive. The greatest increases, from **2p** to **3p** and from **4p** to **5p,** correlate with especially large increases in radii. In the short rows of the table there is a tightening up to the right, due to increasing nuclear charge. In the long rows the same effect occurs, but with a reversal in the right-central region. An explanation for this trend in the sizes of metal atoms was already offered in Section 2–2. The interruptions of the general trend at Eu, Yb, and Am represent the achievement of closed half-subshells with two loosely held valence electrons rather than three or more tightly held ones.

The polarization and refractivity discussed up to now have been electronic, arising from the ability of electrons in atoms to follow somewhat the electromagnetic undulations of light passing through. Extrapolation to infinite wavelength makes it possible to include the small additional contributions of electrons at the lower frequencies. But it turns out that this procedure does not quite predict, for molecules, the total refractivity found by actual measurements in the infrared. The extra amount is due to the ability of entire atoms, with whatever fractional charge they carry, to vibrate at frequencies below that of visible light. In the absence of many accurate measurements, this vibrational polarization has sometimes been assumed to be about 20% of the total.

Vibrational (and total) refractivity should depend on the magnitude of localized dipoles, which must partly depend, in

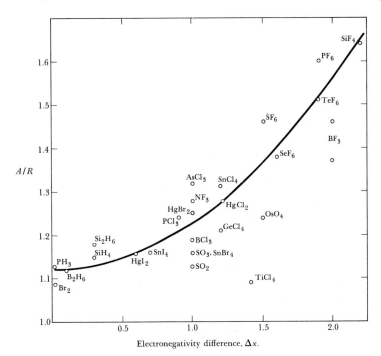

Fig. 4–1. Ratio of total to optical refractivity versus difference of Pauling electronegativities. Curve: $A/R = 1.12 + .11(\Delta x)^2$.

turn, on electronegativity differences. A first-power dependence is ruled out since the refractivity must be positive, regardless of which atom is positive or negative. We therefore present in Fig. 4–1 an empirical correlation of the ratio of total refractivity A to R with the square of the Pauling electronegativity differences. The simple inorganic molecules included are the ones for which both A and R are given in a Bureau of Standards compilation.[7] There are large deviations from the curve, but certainly less than if we simply assumed a constant 20% difference between A and R. It must be said, too, that refractivities reported by various experimenters often show rather wild variations. A more fundamental problem, however, is that the interaction of radiation with molecular vibrations does not depend simply on electronegativity differences, or even on localized or over-all dipole moments (μ), but on $d\mu/dq$, where q is the vibration coordinate.

Consequently, Fig. 4–1 suggests that the correlation among these is limited, although of some value.

4-2 POLARIZING STRENGTH

For the polarizing strengths of ions with inert-gas structures, Grinberg[8] assigns the values in Table 4–2. These are based on a simple electrostatic model, assuming the force on a test charge at the surface of the ion to be proportional to $|Z|/r^2$, or absolute charge over the square of ionic radius. This is reminiscent of Allred and Rochow's definition of electronegativity, but without correction for the "effectiveness" of the charge. (Note that the vertical trend is, as it must be, contrary to that observed in the ability to be polarized.) Admittedly, this underestimates the ability of ions like Ag^+ to polarize others.

For the cations, this kind of table provides a partial explanation of the often mentioned diagonal relationship, that is, the similarity of some properties along a diagonal from upper left to lower right (but see Chapter 8, Reference 15 on $|Z|/r$). An example would be Be^{2+}, Al^{3+}, and Ti^{4+}, whose hydroxides are all very weakly basic and even less acidic, and which react alike with some organic reagents, for example.

Ahrens, in a brief note,[9] suggested measuring polarizing strengths of cations by their electron affinities (ionization energies of the ions or atoms with one less positive charge). This would put them in the following order, starting with the smallest electron affinity: Cs^+, Rb^+, K^+, Na^+, Li^+, Tl^+, Ag^+, Cu^+, Au^+, Ba^{2+}, Sr^{2+}, Ca^{2+}, H^+, Sn^{2+}, Pb^{2+}, Mg^{2+}, Mn^{2+}, Fe^{2+}, Cd^{2+}, Co^{2+}, Zn^{2+}, Ni^{2+}, Be^{2+}, Hg^{2+}, Pd^{2+}, Cu^{2+}, La^{3+}, and so on. If restricted to series of constant oxidation state, as in the original note, this arrangement has some value for chemistry,

Table 4-2 *Polarizing Strength,* $\dfrac{|Z|}{r^2}$

				Li^+	1.7	Be^{2+}	16				
O^{2-}	1.1	F^-	.6	Na^+	1.0	Mg^{2+}	3.3	Al^{3+}	9.2	Si^{4+}	26
S^{2-}	.7	Cl^-	.3	K^+	.6	Ca^{2+}	1.8	Sc^{3+}	4.4	Ti^{4+}	9.8
Se^{2-}	.5	Br^-	.3	Rb^+	.5	Sr^{2+}	1.2	Y^{3+}	2.7	Zr^{4+}	5.3
Te^{2-}	.5	I^-	.2	Cs^+	.4	Ba^{2+}	1.0	La^{3+}	2.0	Ce^{4+}	3.8
										Th^{4+}	3.3

although some positions are still problematical; but if taken to the logical conclusion, as here, it certainly produces some strange combinations—for example, Au^+, Ba^{2+}; or Be^{2+}, Hg^{2+}; or Cu^{2+}, La^{3+}.

Further progress seems to require a recognition that cations have at least two kinds of polarizing strength. One is seen best in ions such as Li^+ or Be^{2+}, whose iodides, for example, have little covalent character, but whose aqueous forms are considerably hydrolyzed because of polarization of water molecules. These cations are all in that part of the periodic table where structures isoelectronic to the noble gases are found. With these structures it is reasonable to assign the ability to polarize mainly to an electrostatic effect.

Ag^+ and Hg^{2+} represent the other kind of polarizing strength. This kind results in a greater covalency of bonding with the oxidizable or iodide type of anion and it is associated with the highly reducible cations found near the center of the periodic table. These are also the ones that have high electron affinities for their charge and size. One trouble with using a scale based on electron affinity alone is that a large component of this affinity results from the ordinary or long-range electrostatic attraction operating at considerable distances beyond the immediate neighborhood, while we need to identify the second component, which is apparently a short-range effect due to penetration of the d subshell by nearby electrons.

These considerations suggest correcting the electron affinity by subtracting the part that would be expected for a noble-gas, or 8-electron, cation of the same charge and size accepting an electron into its lowest s orbital. This is easily done by reference to Fig. 3–2 and tables of ionic radii. Furthermore, since relationships appear to be more significant than absolute values, we propose to define the "excess polarizing strength" as $(E_a - E_n)/E_n$ where E_a and E_n are respectively the actual and noble-gas electron affinities. Results are given in Table 4–3. Note a somewhat different correction by Williams (Chapter 8, Reference 7b), who defined an $R \equiv E_a/(100z^2/r)$.

In the table the heaviest metals do have some of the largest values, corresponding to their known tendencies toward covalency, deeply colored compounds, and so on. The values for **s1**, **s2**, **2p**, and **3p** elements (not included in the table) are zero, practically by definition. Values for Cr^{2+} (using an interpolated

Table 4-3 Excess Polarizing Strength, Eps

	Sc	Ti	V	Cr	Mn	Fe	Co	Ni	Cu	Zn	Ga	Ge	As	Se	Br
5+			0.43												
4+		0.31	0.39												
3+	0.15	0.23	0.29	0.23	0.38	0.23	0.34	0.24	0.42	0.27	0.21	0.18	0.15	0.07	0.11
2+			0.15	0.26?	0.16	0.15	0.20		0.50			0.11	0.07		
1+															

	Y	Zr				Pd	Ag	Cd	In	Sn	Sb	Te
5+												
4+		0.16										
3+	0.04					0.54	0.70	0.41	0.30	0.28	0.27	0.2?
2+							0.68			0.19	0.13	
1+												

	La			Au	Hg	Tl	Pb	Bi
5+								
4+								
3+	0.10			1.14	0.59	0.53	0.49	0.44
2+						0.46	0.42	0.30
1+								

66

radius, 0.84 Å) and Mn^{3+} show the effect of being one electron short of a half-full subshell. The value for Co^{3+}, like all the others except Pd^{2+}, is based on the high-spin spectroscopic ground state in the absence of other information. In most chemical compounds, however, the cobalt(III) ion has all its electrons paired. For palladium(II) it was possible to correct for the energy of pairing, giving a value again applicable to most of its compounds.

If we apply these values to chemical correlations, we have to be careful to include any other relevant considerations. For example, we might predict, from Table 4–3, that bismuthate and vanadate should have similar oxidizing properties, whereas actually bismuthate is by far the stronger one. The chemical reduction of bismuthate involves two electrons, however, and certainly the unstable intermediate Bi^{4+} (radius unknown) must have a high excess polarizing strength, because its electron affinity (45.3 eV) is more than the average of those for the 5 + and 3 + oxidation states (56.0 and 24.56 eV).

As another cautionary example, but considering now the ability of polarization to produce color not present in separate ions, we note that CoS is much darker than CdS, even though the cadmium cation has the greater excess polarizing strength. Here an additional factor is the interaction of unpaired electrons among the poorly separated cobalt cations. See Section 7–3.

Table 4–3 should nevertheless be of some use, together with others, in explaining electrode potentials, acidities, complex-dissociation constants, colors, and other phenomena. At this writing, its applications have not been worked out. No corresponding measure for anions or complex ions is proposed here.

The two kinds of polarizing strengths of cations could perhaps be divided somewhat differently as acidity and reducibility. For anions, in turn, we might then define a basicity and some kind of one-electron oxidizability or ionization energy. Edwards (Chapter 8, Reference 11) has already correlated rates of substitution reactions with basicity and (earlier) oxidation potential or (later) polarizability of one reagent, together with empirical constants for the other.

4-3 BOILING POINT AND POLARIZABILITY

General

Boiling points have often been correlated empirically with the constitution and structure of compounds and with various other properties.[10] Most of these correlations have been restricted to organic compounds or even to homologous series. Many of them involve molecular weight or purely *ad hoc* boiling point numbers. Figure 4–2 is presented here to dispel the common idea that molecular weight, by itself, is an important determinant of intermolecular forces and boiling points.

In order to isolate molecular weight as a factor, we have to study series of nonpolar molecules whose outer atoms are the same, or at least have the same polarizability, but whose central atoms of different weights are well shielded from neighboring molecules. Such series are connected in the graph by solid lines. The usual series that are supposed to show the importance of molecular weight are connected by dashed lines. The latter series, of course, show large differences of molecular volume and polarizability of exposed atoms in addition to the differences in molecular weight.

In the organometallic compounds the poorly shielded central atoms of the tetramethyl series do show some influence on boiling points, but this influence disappears if the methyl groups are replaced by the larger propyl or phenyl groups.

Actually, a slight effect of molecular weight, as such, is known in the fact that deuterium compounds have boiling points a degree or two higher than the ordinary hydrogen analogs. This effect has nothing to do with the negligible gravitational forces but derives from the quantum-mechanical zero-point vibrational energy and practically disappears in heavier elements.

For predicting boiling points, molecular weight, when it works, *has* had the practical advantage of being more accessible than polarizability or molar refraction. Moreover, when it is used in very restricted classes of compounds, it is sometimes possible to attain high accuracy of prediction.

In contrast to the purely empirical relations mentioned above are a few comprehensive theories founded on basic principles of quantum and statistical mechanics. Application of these to the liquid state naturally brings great mathematical difficul-

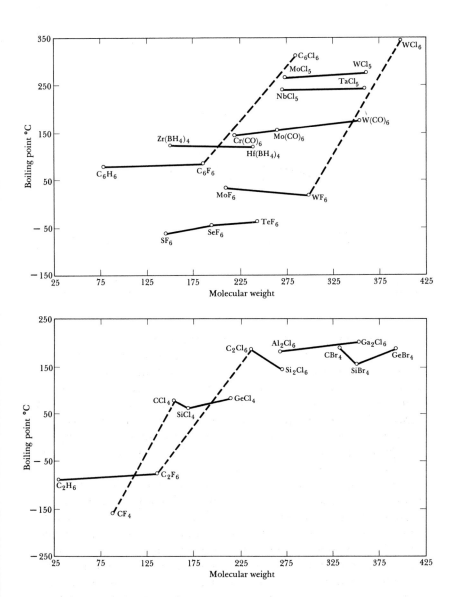

ties and calls for severe approximations but results in real under-standing. Eyring's theory,[11] for example, can give a variety of thermodynamic and kinetic quantities in simple cases although several of these quantities are first required as input information.

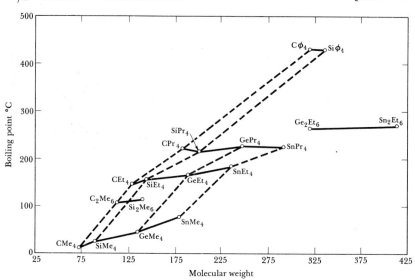

Fig. 4–2. Nondependence of boiling point on molecular weight *per se.*

The approach followed here is much more empirical than Eyring's and is restricted to one thermodynamic parameter, but it has both the qualitative theoretical justification and also the generality (in regard to type of substance covered) lacking in earlier purely empirical relations. The calculations are usually simple. This method does not require previous thermodynamic information on new substances, but only some knowledge of structure; therefore it can often be applied to predicted but unknown substances of a wide variety.

Why should boiling point depend on polarizability or refractivity? Boiling points are determined primarily by the strength of intermolecular forces. Entropy effects are smaller (and harder to evaluate). Intermolecular forces, in turn, depend both on permanent dipoles, quadrupoles, and so on, and on temporary n-poles induced, in proportion to polarizability, by neighboring molecules. By omitting molecules having sizeable permanent dipoles or quadrupoles, as in the present treatment, we can then discover the expected correlation.

London derived the relation $E = (3/4)(\alpha^2 h\nu_0/r^6)$. It has been pointed out that $h\nu_0$ does not vary much from 230 kcal/mole.[12] Therefore, the energy and force between two identical molecules at a given distance should vary with polarizability squared. But larger polarizability means larger size; therefore, molecules in contact, as in a liquid, will show less than a second-power dependence. This, and the fact that the London relation is inaccurate at contact distances, are two reasons for an empirical approach.

Scope

We can summarize the scope of the correlation to be given simply by noting the exclusion of all molecules influenced significantly by other than these "London" (or "van der Waals" or "dispersion" or "mutual polarization") forces. To be more specific, we have the following particular exclusions, with some examples in each case:

1. The liquid (or solid, in sublimation) is nonmolecular: $Cu(NO_3)_2$, C.

2. Considerable decomposition or depolymerization occurs during boiling, showing the participation of chemical bonding forces in the phase change: $N_2O_2(l) = 2NO(g)$. $Ga_2I_6(l) = 2GaI_3(g)$.

3. Metallic properties are appreciable, indicating the availability of empty orbitals for metallic bonding in the condensed phases. In addition to the accepted metals, I_2, with its metallic luster, could thus be excluded.

4. Dipole moments are greater than 1×10^{-18} esu: N_2O_5, BH_3CO, and $AsCl_3$.

5. Quadruple moments have absolute values greater than 2×10^{-26} esu:[13-14] CO_2, N_2O, XeF_2 (Chapter 1, Reference 16), and C_2H_2. Related substances with unknown quadrupole moments have also been excluded: C_5O_2, C_2HBr.

6. Quantum mechanics causes significant deviation of the translational degrees of freedom from classical behavior:[15a] only H_2, He, and Ne.

Two types of exclusions have nothing to do with intermolecular forces. First, some classes of compounds, for example organic, are too numerous to be completely included in Fig. 4–3. Second, some interesting substances had to be omitted because of ignorance concerning either the dipole moments—OF_2, $P(SCN)_3$, NO_2Cl, $FClO_4$, $Fe(NO)_3Cl$, IF_5—or concerning the adequacy of shielding of some atoms: $(PNF_2)_x$, $(CH_3)_3B_3O_3$. The latter ques-

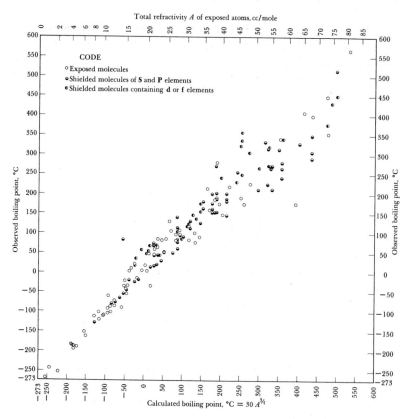

Total refractivity A of exposed atoms, cc/mole

CODE
○ Exposed molecules
◐ Shielded molecules of **S** and **P** elements
◑ Shielded molecules containing **d** or **f** elements

Observed boiling point, °C

Calculated boiling point, °C = $30\, A^{3/4}$

Entries in the graph

	A cm³/mol	calc. bp, °C	obs. bp, °C		A cm³/mol	calc. bp, °C	obs. bp, °C
Highly exposed molecules with experimental total refractivities:							
He[a]	.521	−255	−269	C_4H_4S	24.4	57	84
Ne[a]	1.00	−243	−246	C_6H_6	26.9	82	80
Ar	4.15	−186	−186	$p\text{-}C_6H_4(NO_2)_2$	46.5	260	173
Kr	6.26	−154	−151	$p\text{-}C_6H_4(CN)_2$	48.4	277	225
Xe	10.09	−103	−109				
H_2[a]	2.04	−222	−253	Related:			
O_2	3.96	−189	−183	C_4H_4Se	(28.0)	92	108
O_3	8.1	−129	−112	$[28.0 = A(\text{thiophene}) + 1.12\Delta R(\text{Se} - \text{S})]$			
N_2	4.40	−182	−195				
CO	4.98	−173	−190	Nonflat molecules:			
C_2N_2	14.5	−50	−21	NF_3	9.07	−116	−120
N_2O_4	16.87	−23	21	PCl_3	32.2	133	77
BF_3	8.90	−118	−101	PH_3	12.21	−77	−86
ClF_3	15.94	−33	11	SiF_4	13.75	−59	−90
$B_3N_3H_6$	23.8	51	53	CH_4	6.53	−150	−161
$(HCO_2H)_2$	32.	131	100	C_2H_6	11.21	−89	−89
C_2H_4	10.8	−94	−104	$(CH_2)_3$	14.28	−52	−34

Exposed molecules, using calculated refractivities and the electronegativity correction:

F_2	-183	-188	naphthalene	221	218
Cl_2	-41	-34	anthracene	353	340
Br_2	29	59	phenanthrene	353	340
I_2	185	184	chrysene	474	448
ClF	-87	-101	B_2H_6	-94	-92
$BrCl$	-5	5	B_4H_{10}	3	18
ICl	92	97	B_5H_9	12	48
IBr	117	81	B_5H_{11}	36	63
P_4	190	280	B_6H_{10}	45	82
S_8	436	398[b]	$B_{10}H_{14}$	165	213
HI	18	-35	SiH_4	-107	-112
H_2S	-93	-60	Si_2H_6	-18	-14
H_2Se	-48	-42	$Zn(CH_3)_2$	27	46
AsH_3	-45	-55	$Cd(CH_3)_2$	70	106
P_2H_4	51	52	$Hg(CH_3)_2$	82	96
PBr_3	195	173	$Zn(C_2H_5)_2$	118	118
P_4O_6	393	173!	$Hg(C_2H_5)_2$	170	159
P_4S_3	414	407	$Zn(C_3H_7)_2$	203	146[c]
As_4S_4	532	565	$Hg(C_3H_7)_2$	252	190[c]
NO_2F	-77	-72	$N(CH_3)_3$	8	4
Cl_2O	-39	4	$N(C_2H_5)_3$	145	90[c]
XeO_4	35	85[b]			
OsO_4	66	130			
P_4O_{10}	477	353[c]			

	calc. bp, °C	obs. bp, °C		calc. bp, °C	obs. bp, °C

Shielded molecules of mainly **p** elements; shielded atoms italicized:

	calc. bp, °C	obs. bp, °C		calc. bp, °C	obs. bp, °C
$B(CH_3)_3$	-39	-20	$Ge(C_2H_5)_4$	177	160
$Si(CH_3)_4$	17	27	$Sn(C_2H_5)_4$	177	175
$Ge(CH_3)_4$	17	43	$Pb(C_2H_5)_4$	177	200
$B(C_2H_5)_3$	91	95	$Ge(C_3H_7)_4$	320	225[c]
$Si_2(CH_3)_6$	120	112	$Sn(C_3H_7)_4$	320	225[c]
$Al_2(CH_3)_6$	120	130	$Ge_2(C_2H_5)_6$	329	265[c]
$Si(C_2H_5)_4$	177	152	$Sn_2(C_2H_5)_6$	329	270[c]

Refractivities of fluorides include $\frac{1}{4}R$ of the shielded atoms:

	calc. bp, °C	obs. bp, °C		calc. bp, °C	obs. bp, °C
CF_4	-128	-128	CF_3SF_5	-13	-19
PF_5	-83	-80	IF_7	-23	-25
C_2F_6	-73	-77	$(CF_3)_2SF_4$	33	20
SF_6	-63	-66	S_2F_{10}	43	29
SeF_6	-54	-55	C_6F_{12}	74	50
TeF_6	-43	-44	$CF_2(SF_5)_2$	86	60

	calc. bp, °C	obs. bp, °C		calc. bp, °C	obs. bp, °C
BCl_3	17	13	PCl_5	153	162
$SiCl_4$	86	60	Si_2Cl_6	214	145
CCl_4	86	77	Al_2Cl_6	214	180
$GeCl_4$	86	83	C_2Cl_6	214	187
$SnCl_4$	86	114	Ga_2Cl_6	214	201
B_4Cl_4	86	140[d]	Si_3Cl_8	331	211[c]
$SbCl_5$	153	180	C_3Cl_8	331	270[c]
BBr_3	102	90	$SnBr_4$	189	202
$SiBr_4$	189	153	Si_2Br_6	358	240[c]
$GeBr_4$	189	187	Al_2Br_6	358	263[c]
CBr_4	189	190	Ga_2Br_6	358	279[c]
BI_3	297	210[c]	CI_4	433	307[c]
SiI_4	433	290[c]	SnI_4	433	348[c]
$Si(SCN)_4$	321[e]	314	$B(OCH_3)_3$	25	68
$C(NO_2)_4$	147[f]	126	$B(N(CH_3)_2)_3$	181	152
Cl_2O_7	-57	82[g]	$Be_4O(C_2H_3O_2)_6$	315	331
$P_3N_3Cl_6$	242	256	$Be(C_5H_7O_2)_2$[h]	188	270[d]
$P_4N_4Cl_8$	402	328[c]	$Al(C_5H_7O_2)_3$[h]	350	314
$CSCl_2$	25	73	$Cr(C_5H_7O_2)_3$[h]	350	340
P_4S_{10}	499	514	$Th(C_5H_7O_2)_4$[h]	500	450[b]

Shielded molecules of **d** elements, including R of the shielded atoms:

	calc. bp, °C	obs. bp, °C		calc. bp, °C	obs. bp, °C
MoF_6	20	35	OsF_6	9	48
WF_6	21	17	IrF_6	12	53
UF_6	7	57	PtF_6	16	68
$Fe(C_5H_5)_2$	255	249	ReF_7	33	69[b]
$Ni(CO)_4$	41[i]	43	$Cr(CO)_6$	127[i]	145
$Fe(CO)_5$	87[i]	103	$Mo(CO)_6$	148[i]	156
$Ru(CO)_5$	97[i]	85[b]	$W(CO)_6$	149[i]	175

	calc. $bp, °C$	obs. $bp, °C$			calc. $bp, °C$	obs. $bp, °C$
Shielded molecules including $\frac{1}{2}R$ of the shielded atoms:						
$TiCl_4$	136	136		WCl_6	255	336
$NbCl_5$	201	241		Fe_2Cl_6	275	305
$TaCl_5$	201	242		Au_2Cl_6	300	265
$TiBr_4$	240	230		$NbBr_5$	324	270
$ZrBr_4$	255	357[g]		$TaBr_5$	324	320
$HfBr_4$	252	322		$Al(BH_4)_3$	36	44
TiI_4	473	377[c]		$Zr(BH_4)_4$	114	123
ZrI_4	486	431		$Hf(BH_4)_4$	112	118

[a]Could be excluded (see text).
[b]Extrapolated.
[c]Probable crowding of outer atoms or incomplete exposure of central atoms.
[d]Probable incomplete shielding.
[e]$R(SCN) = 13.40$ (Vogel[16]).
[f]$A(NO_2) = \frac{1}{2}A(N_2O_4)$.
[g]May need reinvestigation.
[h]Acetylacetonates.
[i]$R(CO) = R(C) + R(O)$.

Fig. 4–3. Correlation of boiling point with refractivity of exposed atoms. A dash between the code number and the formula of an exposed molecule indicates that the total refraction is from Reference 7; otherwise the source is Table 4–1.

tion may arise because of uncertain geometry but is more common where structural complications make geometric calculations, explained below, uncertain. Sometimes scale models are useful. Where the dipole moment has not been measured, a knowledge of the molecular symmetry may help. The moment must be exactly zero if and only if the molecule has either an alternating axis of symmetry of order higher than 1 or more than one simple axis of symmetry of order higher than 1. Note that an alternating axis of order 2 is equivalent to a center of inversion.

Exposure of Atoms

Since the calculation of boiling points will involve the refractivities of exposed atoms, we turn now to the criteria of exposure. Atoms will be considered exposed if they can touch equivalent atoms in neighboring molecules; otherwise they are said to be shielded. To determine this we calculate, for symmetrical molecules with the formula MX_n, the minimum separation between two M atoms when the two molecules containing them fit together as closely as possible. The surfaces are defined by the van der Waals radii when available (Table 2–1) and by the co-valent radii plus 0.8 Å otherwise (Chapter 2, Reference 2).

A negative result for the minimum separation of two atoms is taken to mean that these two can overlap each other before all the other atoms considered in the calculations have approached as closely as possible. For example, the Zr atoms in $ZrCl_4$ are found by this criterion to be exposed and to be able to overlap before the chlorine atoms in neighboring molecules have come into maximum contact *either* with the neighboring chlorine atoms *or* with the neighboring zirconium atom. This is taken to mean that London forces between neighboring zirconium atoms will contribute significantly to the total intermolecular forces and that the refractivity of zirconium has to be included in the calculations given below. In contrast, the Sn atoms in $SnCl_4$ are found to be (barely) shielded. The boiling point of $SnCl_4$ can therefore be calculated fairly well using only the refractivity of chlorine. Obviously, it would be better to have a way of includ-ing atoms partially but this has not been tried, except as below.

Minimum separations between the atom M and the atom X in neighboring molecules have also been calculated. The results, however, show that even when the neighboring M and X can touch each other there is no appreciable influence on boiling point if the M atoms are shielded from each other.

The minimum separation of the M atoms in two molecules MX_n corresponds to contact between three X atoms (two in MX_2) in one molecule and either three X atoms in the other molecule or the M atom in the other molecule, whichever has to make con-tact first as the molecules approach each other. The larger of the two calculated separations is therefore the actual minimum value. In Fig. 4–3 the dividing line between exposure and shield-ing has been taken to be -0.06 Å since it has been found that molecules whose central atoms are calculated to overlap up to 0.06 Å behave as if shielded.

Table 4–4 gives the formulas derived from solid geometry for these calculations.

For symmetrical carbonyls, $M(CO)_n$, the formulas can still be used with slight modifications. Then v_X is the van der Waals radius of carbon $(= v_C)$ for calculating M—M separations and c is the M—C bond distance. The formulas for M—X separation, however, require substitution of $(v_C + v_O)^2$ for $4v_X^2$ and of $v_O + v_M$ for $v_X + v_M$, writing v_O for the van der Waals radius of oxy-

Table 4-4 *Minimum Distances*

	M-M with X-X contact	M-M with M-X contact	M-X with X-X contact
Planar	$\sqrt{4v_X^2 - (2 - \sqrt{2 + 2\cos\alpha}\,)c^2} - 2v_M$	$\sqrt{(v_X + v_M)^2 - c^2} - 2v_M$	$\sqrt{4v_X^2 - c^2} - (v_X + v_M)$
Regular Polyhedral	$\sqrt{4v_X^2 - \dfrac{2 - 2\cos\alpha}{3}\,c^2} \;+\; 2\sqrt{\dfrac{1 + 2\cos\alpha}{3}}\;c - 2v_M$	$\sqrt{(v_X + v_M)^2 - \dfrac{2 - 2\cos\alpha}{3}\,c^2} \;+\; \sqrt{\dfrac{1 + 2\cos\alpha}{3}}\;c - 2v_M$	$\sqrt{4v_X^2 - \dfrac{2 - 2\cos\alpha}{3}\,c^2} \;+\; \sqrt{\dfrac{1 + 2\cos\alpha}{3}}\;c - (v_X + v_M)$
Symmetrical Bipyramidal	$\sqrt{4v_X^2 - \dfrac{2 - 2\cos\alpha}{3 + \cos\alpha}\,c^2} \;+\; 2\sqrt{\dfrac{1 + \cos\alpha}{3 + \cos\alpha}}\;c - 2v_M$	$\sqrt{(v_X + v_M)^2 - \dfrac{2}{3 + \cos\alpha}\,c^2} \;+\; \sqrt{\dfrac{1 + \cos\alpha}{3 + \cos\alpha}}\;c - 2v_M$	$\sqrt{4v_X^2 - \dfrac{2}{3 + \cos\alpha}\,c^2} \;+\; \sqrt{\dfrac{1 + \cos\alpha}{3 + \cos\alpha}}\;c - (v_X + v_M)$

$c =$ covalent radius sum, or actual M—X bond distance where known.

$v_X, v_M =$ van der Waals radii for X and M, respectively.

$\alpha =$ angle XMX for adjacent X atoms. In bipyramidal molecules it refers only to the equatorial atoms, the other angles being 90°.

gen. Some other cases can be readily dealt with by using slight simplifications. Au_2Cl_6, for example, can be assumed to have a perfectly square planar geometry for each gold atom.

Results

The correlation in Fig. 4–3 is the evidence for the equation:[*] bp $= (30A^{3/4} - 273)°$. For molecules in which all atoms are exposed, A is the total refractivity. Some of these values are obtainable directly from the compilation of Maryott and Buckley.[7] Otherwise, we can calculate the total R from Table 4–1 and use the formula of Fig. 4–1 to correct to A. For some substances such as NO_2F the question is what electronegativity difference to use. The refraction in Fig. 4–3 was based on R for NO_2 and the electronegativity difference (Table 3–1) between F and the average for one N and two O's. Procedures now being developed (References 10, 16, and 17 in Chapter 3) may answer this question more satisfactorily in the future.

For unsaturated molecules we need to consider the extra polarizability of the π electrons. With a group like NO_2, just mentioned, we can simply use the total observed R. Where this is not known or where, as in the acetylacetonates, part of the group is shielded, we use a double-bond increment for R, given by Vogel[16] as 1.575.

For shielded molecules except as below the total refractivity is taken as the sum of the total atomic refractivities of all except the shielded atoms. With the acetylacetonates, the central atom and the oxygens are considered shielded. Each ring in these is counted as having one exposed double bond. In ferrocene each ring is assigned five unsaturation electrons or $2\frac{1}{2}$ double bonds and the iron atom is assumed exposed.

For the elementary halogens and their compounds, especially with the transition metals, much better results are obtained, as in Fig. 4–3, if the halogen refractivities are increased 20% above the values in Table 4–1, and if part of the refractivity of the central atom (when present) is included. As seen in the legend of the figure, other compounds of **d** elements can also be grouped according to the shielding available. The following are

---

[*] Some of the calculations were performed by Erwin Boschmann and Russell Yost.

the percentages of the central atom that are included for otherwise shielded halides:

	F	Cl	Br	I
p elements	25%	0	0	0
d elements	100%	50%	50%	50%

Quantitatively the corrections are certainly empirical, but qualitatively it is entirely reasonable that the smaller halogen atoms
shield the central atom less adequately than do larger atoms or
groups of atoms. A final correction, for which no nonempirical
rationalization seems available, is that only 50% of the refractivities of boron and silicon are used in any calculations involving these elements (when exposed). The low boiling points of
silicon compounds have been noted before, with various interpretations.[15b,17]

The lower left side of the graph reveals many exposed substances whose boiling points are lower than calculated. Most of
these contain central atoms surrounded on all sides but not
quite enough to be considered shielded. Some iodides also boil
too low, and this may be due to crowding, with a consequent lack
of full exposure of even the outer atoms.

The normal boiling point of sulfur was not used because
the liquid starts turning dark above 160° and is not at all pure
S_8. Extrapolation of the vapor pressure up to 160° yields an estimated boiling point of 398° for S_8, as used in the diagram.
Values for $Ru(CO)_5$, XeO_4, ReF_7, and $ThAcac_4$ also had to be obtained by extrapolation.

Formic acid is of some interest because the vapor remains
largely dimeric at the boiling point and because the total refractivity of the dimer, 32 cc, is reported to be much more than twice
the optical refractivity of the monomer, 8.5 cc. This would still
be so even with a modest allowance for the infrared, but the
value for the dimer fits fairly well in Fig. 4–3.

Melting points have not yet been examined as above because in addition to the considerations already mentioned, symmetry and other effects become very important. These and other
thermodynamic parameters should be studied further, together
with purely theoretical investigations.

4-4 ENERGY AND ENTROPY OF ATOMIZATION

Oxidation or reduction of an element to an aqueous ion can be analyzed into simpler steps, illustrated by magnesium:

$$1.\ Mg(s) \rightarrow Mg(g)$$
$$2.\ Mg(g) \rightarrow Mg^{2+} + 2e^-$$
$$3.\ Mg^{2+} + 6\ H_2O \rightarrow Mg(OH_2)_6{}^{2+}$$

The first step, sublimation for a metal or dissociation for a poly-atomic gas, can be called atomization. The second and third steps are discussed in Sections 3–1 and 5–3. Chapter 6 deals partly with the over-all process.

The thermodynamic components[20-21] of atomization are given in Table 4–5. Study of the rows suggests a strong correlation of the energy requirement with valence. The dips at manganese and the d10 elements occur where two s electrons are still available for metallic bonding but the d subshell is exactly half full or full, respectively. In the latter case the d subshell seems to become completely unavailable for bonding. The effect is smaller with manganese and negligible with technetium and rhenium; in the latter cases this reflects the irrelevance of half-completeness, due to electron pairing. The dips do not coincide with maximum metallic radii or minimum metallic valences of the type discussed in Section 2–2. Yet they do occur at the elements that form especially stable bivalent ions.

As we go down the columns, the heat of atomization usually decreases for s, p and d10 groups of elements and increases for most d groups. The covalent and metallic radii simultaneously increase (only slightly in d columns) so that interatomic attractive forces must operate over greater average distances, especially for s and p elements. An important opposing factor for all the heavier elements, particularly in the dense d series, may be the greater London (mutual polarization) forces among atoms with more electrons. Such forces are weak in substances with complete outer shells but the free valence electrons in metals hold the atoms much closer together and the mutual polarization forces vary approximately as the inverse seventh power of the distance.

Whatever may be the cause of strong metal-metal bonding among the heavy transition elements, the same phenomenon is observed in certain complex ions. Some now known would include $Hg_2{}^{2+}$, $Mo_6Cl_8{}^{4+}$, and $Re_3Cl_{12}{}^{3-}$. This tendency to unite

Table 4-5 *Thermodynamics of Atomization*

ΔH, kcal/gram-atom
ΔS, cal/gram-atom degree
ΔG or ΔF, kcal/gram-atom

Values listed for each element as: ΔH / ΔS / ΔG(or ΔF)

Element	ΔH	ΔS	ΔG
H	52	12	49
Li	38	26	31
Be	78	30	69
Na	26	25	19
Mg	36	28	27
K	21	23	15
Ca	42	27	34
Sc	82	33	72
Ti	113	36	102
V	123	36	112
Cr	95	37	84
Mn	67	34	57
Fe	100	37	89
Co	102	36	91
Ni	101	36	90
Cu	81	32	72
Zn	31	30	23
Ga	65	33	56
Ge	90	33	80
As	69	33	59
Se	49	32	40
Br	27	24	20
Rb	20	23	13
Sr	39	26	31
Y	102	32	92
Zr	146	34	136
Nb	178	36	167
Mo	158	37	147
Tc	155	35	144
Ru	144	38	133
Rh	133	37	122
Pd	94	31	85
Ag	68	31	59
Cd	27	28	18
In	57	27	49
Sn	72	28	64
Sb	63	32	53
Te	47	32	37
I	25	29	17
Cs	19	22	12
Ba	42	26	34
Lu	67	32	56
Hf	168	34	158
Ta	187	34	177
W	200	34	190
Re	186	36	175
Os	160	38	149
Ir	150	38	139
Pt	135	36	124
Au	85	32	75
Hg	15	23	8
Tl	43	28	35
Pb	47	26	39
Bi	48	31	38
Po	34	30	25
At	22	30	13
Fr	17	21	11
Ra	39	25	31
B	141	35	130
C	172	36	160
N	113	12	109
O	60	14	55
F	19	14	15
Al	78	33	68
Si	105	36	94
P	80	32	70
S	57	32	47
Cl	29	13	25

Lanthanides:

Element	ΔH	ΔS	ΔG
La	100	30	91
Ce		34	
Nd	77	28	69
Sm	50	27	42
Eu	43	28	35
Gd	82	31	73
Yb	43	26	35

Pr, Pm, Tb, Dy, Ho, Er, Tm — (no values listed)

Actinides:

Element	ΔH	ΔS	ΔG
Th		34	
U	117	36	107

Ac, Pa, Np, Pu, Am, Cm, Bk, Cf, Es, Fm, Md, Lw — (no values listed) with atoms of the same kind has, with much felicity, been termed "homophilicity" by F. A. Cotton.[26] The example of mercurous ion makes all the more surprising the inordinately low value of ΔH for the vaporization of mercury. This is related to, but not really explained by, the liquid standard state and low boiling point of the element. The even lower boiling points of some non-metals are, nevertheless, largely irrelevant here because the vapor still contains polyatomic molecules in these cases.

The increase in ΔH between F and Cl, contrary to the trend, has had various rationalizations. However, it is part of a general phenomenon as seen in the unusually small decrease between O and S and between some 4p and 5p elements, and in irregularities of ionization energy, heats of oxidation, stabilities of high oxidation states, and so on (Chapter 3, Reference 8). A factor that may contribute in some of these phenomena is the availability, in late 3p and 5p elements (for example, Cl), of new d and f orbitals for the strengthening of bonds by hybridization or for formation of p-d π bonds.[22-23] Comparison of Figs. 1–1 and 1–3 shows, however, that a positive charge favors the availability of these additional orbitals, which may thus be more relevant to the oxidized species of Section 6–3 than to the elements.

In addition to looking for extra strength in the Cl—Cl bond, we can look for extra weakness in the F—F bond. An important factor appears to be the repulsion of the unshared outer electrons on either atom against those on the other and against the bonding pair. This would be greatest in the smallest atoms and would weaken their σ bonds.

A related question, though not strictly concerned with the atomization of elements, has to do with the prevalence of multiple bonding involving 2p elements (as in CO_2, N_2, $B_3N_3H_6$ and so on) and the paucity of such bonding in their absence. One explanation points out that the heavier atoms have larger *inner* shells with many more electrons.[24] These may prevent the close approaches required for effective multiple bonding. The suggestions of the previous two paragraphs may also be significant here.

Inspection of the entropies of atomization shows similar but much smaller effects, with the exception of the liquid and, especially, the gaseous elements. The absolute entropies at 25° for all but the lightest elements are close to 40 cal/deg mole in the monatomic form. The changes must thus be mainly accounted for by the differences in standard states of the elements. In solids, thermal motion is relatively restricted, leading to low entropies in the standard states. In gases, excluding the noble gases not considered here, the polyatomic molecules have vibrational and rotational degrees of freedom not available after dissociation; hence, the higher entropy of the standard states.

Free energies are not discussed separately in this connection since they are clearly the resultants of the factors already considered.

REFERENCES

1. *Structure and Properties of Solid Surfaces,* eds. R. Gomer and C. S. Smith (U. of Chicago, 1953): J. E. Mayer, p. 181; W. A. Weyl, p. 183, statements on limitations and possibilities of the polarization concept.

2. *The Chemistry of the Coordination Compounds,* ed. J. C. Bailar, Jr. (New York: Reinhold, 1956), R. W. Parry and R. N. Keller, pp. 121–130, etc., "Polarization as a Factor in the Ionic Model."

3. O. K. Rice, *Electronic Structure and Chemical Binding* (New York: McGraw-Hill, 1940), Section 12.4, "Polarizability . . ." and other sections.

4. *Encyclopedia of Chemistry,* ed. G. L. Clark (New York: Reinhold, 1957), K. Fajans, p. 763, "Polarization."

5. M. J. Sienko and R. A. Plane, *Physical Inorganic Chemistry* (New York: Benjamin, 1963), p. 70, Table 2–5, "Electronic Polarizabilities," from L. Pauling, *Proc. Roy. Soc.* (1927), **A114**, 198.

6. S. S. Batsanov, *Refractometry and Chemical Structure* (New York: Consultants Bureau, 1961): p. 29, table of atomic refractivities; pp. 27–28, on refractivities of metals.

7. A. A. Maryott and F. Buckley, *Table of Dielectric Constants and Electric Dipole Moments of Substances in the Gaseous State, Circ. 537* (Washington, D. C.: National Bureau of Standards, 1953).

8. A. A. Grinberg, *An Introduction to the Chemistry of Complex Compounds,* trans. Leach, eds. Busch and Trimble (London: Pergamon, 1962), p. 191, table of polarizing strength, $|Z|/r^2$, but misnamed as a potential.

9. L. H. Ahrens, "Anion Affinity and Polarizing Power of Cations," *Nature* (1952), **169**, 463.

10. J. R. Partington, *An Advanced Treatise on Physical Chemistry* (London: Longmans-Green, 1955), **2**, 295–303, on empirical boiling-point correlations.

11. H. Eyring and R. P. Marchi, "Significant Structure Theory of Liquids," *J. Chem. Ed.* (1963), **40,** 562.

12. Y. K. Syrkin and M. E. Dyatkina, *Structure of Molecules and the Chemical Bond,* trans. and revised by M. A. Partridge and D. O. Jordan (London: Butterworths, 1950), p. 265, on the London relation for intermolecular energies.

13. J. O. Hirschfelder, C. F. Curtiss, and R. B. Bird, *Molecular Theory of Gases and Liquids* (New York: Wiley, 1954): p. 877, **on** quadrupole moments; Section 13.3.a and p. 963 on London dispersion forces.

14. A. D. Buckingham, *Quart. Rev.* (1959), **13**, 204 (on CO_2), 214, on quadrupole moments.

15. (a) J. H. Hildebrand and R. L. Scott, *The Solubility of Non-electrolytes* (New York: Reinhold, 1950), p. 67, mentions the quantum effect on H_2, He and Ne in the liquid state. (b) *Ibid.,* pp. 60–61, on the relation of the low boiling point of $SiCl_4$ to its large volume. Also, Hildebrand, "Forces between Tetrahalide Molecules," *J. Chem. Phys.* (1947), **15,** 727.

16. A. I. Vogel, *J. Chem. Soc.* (1948), 1842, Table XXII, "Atomic, structural and group parachors and refractivities."

17. L. Pauling, *The Nature of the Chemical Bond* (3rd ed., Ithaca, New York: Cornell, 1960), pp. 311–313, on bonding in silicon halides.

18. C. R. Kinney, *J. Am. Chem. Soc.* (1938), **60,** 3032, on boiling point as a linear function of the cube root of *ad hoc* boiling-point numbers.

19. K. S. Pitzer, "Inter- and Intramolecular Forces and Molecular Polarizability," *Adv. Chem. Phys.* (New York: Interscience, 1959), **2,** 59.

20. D. R. Stull and G. C. Sinke, *Thermodynamic Properties of the Elements* (Washington, D.C.: American Chemical Society, 1956).

21. T. L. Cottrell, *The Strengths of Chemical Bonds* (2nd ed., London: Butterworths, 1958).

22. (a) R. S. Mulliken, in "Overlap Integrals and Chemical Bonding," *J. Am. Chem. Soc.* (1950), **72,** 4496. (b) Mulliken, "Structure of the Halogen Molecules and the Strength of Single Bonds," *J. Am. Chem. Soc.* (1955), **77,** 884.

23. D. P. Craig and E. A. Magnusson, "d-Orbital Contraction in Chemical Bonding," including p. 4908, "π-Bonding," *J. Chem. Soc.* (1956), p. 4895.

24. K. S. Pitzer, "Repulsive Forces in Relation to Bond Energies . . . ," *J. Am. Chem. Soc.* (1948), **70**, 2141.

25. N. Engel, "Properties of Metallic Phases as a Function of Number and Kind of Bonding Electrons," *Powder Metallurgy Bulletin* (1957), **7**, 8, found too late to include in text, but facilitates explanation of some trends in Section 4–4 and others. Also consult L. Brewer for further development.

26. F. A. Cotton, *et al.*, "Mononuclear and Polynuclear Chemistry of Rhenium(III): Its Pronounced Homophilicity," *Science* (1964), **145**, 1305, evidence for a quadruple bond.

5

Acidity and Basicity

Starting with this chapter we turn to properties that have more to do with ordinary test-tube chemistry. These, though often neglected in modern discussions of periodicity, will continue to be important as long as chemistry is not absorbed by physics. Of course, the concomitant necessity of considering interactions among several substances or several simpler properties brings both greater difficulty and a keener challenge.

5-1   HYDRO-ACIDS

The very decided trends in the acidities of hydrides of nonmetals[1] are evident in Table 5–1. Before discussing trends, we should clarify the numerical values for water, which may puzzle readers accustomed both to a pK of 14 for its ionization by loss of H^+ and to no pK at all for its ability to attach H^+. By contrast the pK of 3.25 for HF corresponds to the usual $HF \rightarrow H^+ + F^-$ and $(H^+)(F^-)/(HF) = 10^{-3.25}$. (It is understood that these expressions involve activities, not concentrations.) For a fair comparison with water we should write (Equation 5–1)

$$HF + H_2O \rightarrow H_3O^+ + F^-$$

and
$$\frac{(H_3O^+)(F^-)}{(H_2O)\,(HF)} = \frac{10^{-3.25}}{55} = 10^{-4.99} \qquad (5\text{–}1)$$

We usually omit the nearly constant $(H_2O) = 55$ M purely as a convenience. For water itself we have

$$H_2O + H_2O \rightarrow H_3O^+ + OH^-$$

and
$$\frac{(H_3O^+)\,(OH^-)}{(H_2O)^2} = \frac{10^{-14.00}}{(55)^2} = 10^{-17.48} \qquad (5\text{–}2)$$

and $H_3O^+ + H_2O \rightarrow H_2O + H_3O^+$ and, of course, $K = 1$. To be consistent with common practice for all other common acids, we must now multiply the K's for water by 55 or subtract its log, 1.74, from the pK's, as done in Table 5–1.

Table 5–1 pK's for Successive Ionization of Hydro-Acids

	NH_4^+	9.24	H_3O^+	−1.74		
CH_4 ~58	NH_3	~35	H_2O	15.74	HF	3.25
			OH^-	>36, 25		
	PH_4^+	0, −12				
	PH_3	~27	H_2S	7.0	HCl	−7.0
			HS^-	12.9		
			H_2Se	3.9	HBr	−9.0
			HSe^-	11.0		
			H_2Te	2.64	HI	−9.5
			HTe^-	11.0		

The horizontal trend can readily be correlated with electronegativity, or nuclear charge, as has often been done. However, the vertical trend shows the most electronegative atoms forming the weakest acids, so that we have to consider all the factors at work.[2] For the p5 group, the various energy components are listed in Table 5–2. The ionization step is sometimes "split" further into atomic dissociation plus the transfer of an electron from H to X. Dissociation into atoms, however, is not necessarily simpler or more fundamental than into ions, and the latter per-

mits the more concise treatment used here. The whole calculation cannot be viewed as an independent calculation of pK's, because not all the quantities are measurable separately. On the
other hand, it does show the contribution of the various
steps. Clearly, the greater attraction of the small (gaseous) fluoride ion for hydrogen ion is approximately canceled by its
greater attraction (also expected) for water. The balance is
tipped by the ability of the polar HF molecule to form hydrogen
bonds with water and by the structure-making tendency of the
small fluoride ion. The small rise of vaporization energy from
HCl to HI is due mainly to London forces. If space and additional theoretical refinement were available, we would of course
wish to pursue these explanations farther; in any case, less data
are available for the rest of the periodic table, but the frame-
work now at hand is quite useful as an aid to thinking.

Let us again examine the horizontal trend in Table 5–1. In
any row the molecules are isoelectronic and cannot have very different dispersion forces, so the intermolecular (vaporization)
energies, at least below the first row, are unimportant. Likewise,
the entropies and hydration enthalpies, for ions of constant
charge and nearly constant size such as H_2P^-, HS^- and Cl^-, will
not change significantly. On the other hand, the hydrogen is directly attached to atoms of different effective nuclear charge in
the acids considered. This, therefore, has a tremendous influence
on the ionization enthalpy of both gaseous and aqueous molecules. Such influence operates even over the greater distances
in H_3PO_4, H_2SO_4 and $HClO_4$, as seen below.

In recent years it has been shown that compounds of the

Table 5–2   Factors in the Ionization of Aqueous HX (in kcal/mole)

	HF	HCl	HBr	HI
ΔH vaporization from H_2O	11.5	4.2	5.0	5.5
ΔH ionization $(HX_g \rightarrow H_g^+ + X_g^-)$	367.4	330.9	320.5	310.7
ΔH hydration of both ions $(-258$ for $H^+)$	-381.9	-348.8	-340.7	-330.3
$-T\Delta S$ total	6.2	4.0	2.7	1.0
ΔF or ΔG total $(HX_{aq} \rightarrow H_{aq}^+ + X_{aq}^-)$	3.2	$-$ 9.7	$-$ 12.5	$-$ 13.1

type $HCo(CO)_4$ actually have the hydrogen atom attached to the metal atom.[3] Some pK's have been determined, including: $HMn(CO)_5$ (7.1); $H_2Fe(CO)_4$ (4.44 and 14.0); $HCo(CO)_4$ (0). The two stages of acid ionization for the iron compound differ about as expected in the light of Table 5–1. The acidities in this series increase with atomic number, as in the rows of **p** elements. The reasons may be partly different, but the information is hardly enough to support a discussion of periodicity.

Carbon monoxide contains a highly electronegative atom and is consequently more electrophilic in some ways than the cyclopentadienyl radical, although clearly not entirely comparable to it. We are therefore not surprised that $HReCpd_2$, H_2MoCpd_2, and H_2WCpd_2 are basic (the former about as much so as ammonia) and not significantly acidic. H_3TaCpd_2 is essentially neutral, but there are no unshared valence electrons left on the metal atom, according to the inert-gas or 18-electron rule. The near absence of both acidity and basicity may remind us of the elementary fact that these two properties do not have to vary inversely, except within properly defined limits of discussion.

An intermediate type of compound, $H(Cr,Mo,W)Cpd(CO)_3$, is (as expected) very weakly acidic (weaker than acetic acid).

5-2 HYDROXY-ACIDS

Periodicity affects the strengths of hydroxy-acids in various ways, including its effect on oxidation state and coordination number. The latter effects are roughly accounted for by fairly well-known rules[4] which can be summarized as pK of $H_pXO_q^{r-}$ $= 7 + 5(p - q + 2r)$ if $r + p \leqq q$. Table 5–3 gives the deviations of actual values from these estimates. All entries represent equilibria involving dissolved molecules, not the solid state. Most metallic hydroxides have been omitted because of great discordancies in the data and uncertainties in the formulas. Even quite a few of the entries are subject to significant doubt.

Where the values given are fewer than they could be, usually the first ones are given and the last ones are unknown. All are in order of successive ionizations.

There is considerable randomness in the deviations, suggesting experimental errors and/or the lack of important effects of periodicity not already accounted for. The deviations tend to be positive, which could of course be easily rectified by upward

Table 5–3   Differences of pK's of Hydroxy-Acids from Estimated Values

	III	IV	V	VI	VII	VIII
	H_3BO_3 2.2	H_2CO_3 1.8 3.3 $H_2C_2O_4$ -0.6	HNO_2 1.3 1.7 HNO_3 1.7 $H_2N_2O_2$ 0.0	H_2O_2 4.8		
		H_4SiO_4 2.7	HPH_2O_2 -0.9 H_2PHO_3 0.0 -0.3 H_3PO_4 0.1 0.2 $H_4P_2O_6$ 0.2 $H_4P_2O_7$ -1.2 0.3	H_2SO_3 -0.2 0.2 H_2SO_4 1.0 -0.1 $H_2S_2O_6$ 3.2	$HClO$ 0.5 $HClO_2$ 0.0 $HClO_3$ 0.3 $HClO_4$ 0.7	
		H_4GeO_4 2.4	H_3AsO_3 2.4 H_3AsO_4 0.3 0.0 -0.5	H_2SeO_3 0.6 1.3 H_2SeO_4 ? 0.0	$HBrO$ 1.6 $HBrO_3$ 3.	
p elements			H_3SbO_3 5.	H_2TeO_3 0.6 0.7 H_6TeO_6 0.6 -1.6 -2.	HIO 0.6 3.4 HIO_3 0.6 3.8 H_5IO_6 -0.4 1.4 3.0	H_4XeO_6 ? 4. 3.5
d elements			H_3VO_4 2. 2.0 4.5	H_2CrO_4 2.4 2.0 $H_2Cr_2O_7$ H_2MoO_4 4.8 2.1 H_2WO_4 ? 2.1	$HMnO_4$ 2.0 5.8 H_2MnO_4 1.6 4. $HReO_4$ 6.8	H_2FeO_4 4.
f element			H_2UO_4 12.6			

adjustment of the constant 7 in the equation given. It is clear, however, that the transition elements[19] do tend to form somewhat weaker acids than do the p elements. For them the constant 7 could well be changed to about 10. If the value for H_2UO_4 is typical, f elements form even weaker acids. Structural analysis shows two of these oxygens bonded strongly, but the two OH's weakly, to uranium, so that the O—H bond is fairly strong.

A few other individual acids have noteworthy features. Boric acid, which may be $H_2OB(OH)_3$ in solution, probably ionizes by forming $B(OH)_4^-$ instead of $H_2BO_3^-$, but this does not seem to cause any deviation in acidity. The values for H_2CO_3 are based on the actual ionization of H_2CO_3 molecules, not the predominant CO_2, which gives the often quoted practical pK. For polynuclear acids like $H_2C_2O_4$, we estimate the pK for one fragment, that is, HCO_2. The simple equation, however, cannot be applied to ionizations beyond the first. In a case such as $H_2Cr_2O_7$, the bridging oxygen is counted on both fragments. It might seem that this oxygen atom should be considered more like an OH group since it has another atom attached, but acids of this type (cf. $H_4P_2O_7$) are more acidic than otherwise expected, not less.

In HPH_2O_2 and H_2PHO_3 the unionizable hydrogens attached to phosphorus are, of course, not counted in the formula.

The constant 5 in the equation given, representing the effects of oxidation state and net charge, would have to be much larger if a similar equation could be applied to Table 5–1. This is certainly a result of the hydrogen atoms in hydroxy-acids being farther from the central atom.

5-3 HYDRATED CATIONS

Because hydrated cations are found quite widely distributed in the periodic table, we might expect to have considerable material here for a study of periodicity. Unfortunately, however, these supposedly simple and certainly important ions are still, in many cases, poorly known. Measurements of acidity are often complicated by simultaneous hydrolysis in several stages, polymerization, complexing by anions, and uncertainties of activity coefficients. The data[5] in Table 5–4 are therefore mostly not highly reliable. Similar uncertainties in the case of dissolved metallic hydroxides are also so great that most of these

Table 5–4   Approximate pK's for Acid Ionization of Hydrated Cations

← number of electrons beyond noble gas or $s^2 p^6 f^{14}$ →

0	2	3	5	6	7	8	9	10	12	16
H^+ −1.74										
Li^+ 14										
Na^+ 15									Ag^+ 12	Tl^+ 13	I^+ 4
Be^{2+} 6??										
Mg^{2+} 11										
Ca^{2+} 13			Mn^{2+} 11	Fe^{2+} 10	Co^{2+} 10	Ni^{2+} 10	Cu^{2+} 8	Zn^{2+} 10	Sn^{2+} 4	
Sr^{2+} 13									Cd^{2+} 10	Pb^{2+} 8
Ba^{2+} 13									Hg^{2+} 3	
Al^{3+} 5										
Sc^{3+} 5	V^{3+} 3	Cr^{3+} 4	Fe^{3+} 2	Co^{3+} 2				Ga^{3+} 3		Bi^{3+} 2
Y^{3+} 9								In^{3+} 4		
La^{3+} 10								Tl^{3+} 1		

La^{3+} +3.1 Pr^{3+} +1.9 Nd^{3+} +1.7 Sm^{3+} +0.9 Gd^{3+} +0.5 Dy^{3+} −0.3 ← $pK(M^{3+}) - pK(Y^{3+})_{100°}$

0	2	3
Zr^{4+} 0		
Ce^{4+} 1	U^{4+} 1	Pu^{4+} 2
Th^{4+} 4		

were omitted from the previous section. In any case, the hydroxides merely represent a later stage of hydrolysis of the hydrated cations now being discussed. The other stages are also not treated here. Moreover, the separation of equilibrium or free-energy data into enthalpy and entropy effects is too often not yet possible, just as with most other acids considered in this chapter.

The anticipated promotion of acidity by increasing charge is evident in the table; cf. Na^+, Ca^{2+}, Sm^{3+} and Th^{4+}, whose radii are similar (0.97 to 1.02 Å), and which have a noble-gas structure except for the shielded f electrons in samarium ion. Among the noble-gas-type cations in a given oxidation state, it is also clear that the smaller ones are the more acidic ones, again as expected. At constant charge and size, for example Ca^{2+} and Cd^{2+}, the ions with the greater excess polarizing strength (Section 4–2) are the more acidic ones. This will be included in the general discussion of Chapter 8, where we view the acidity of a cation as its ability to bind a particular ligand, i.e., hydroxide ion. Here we can note that the high acidity of I^+, considering its low charge, doubtless reflects its uniquely low coordination number of one, in H_2IO^+.

The acid hydrolysis of 5f ions to form the exceptionally stable MO_2^{n+} has been discussed by Connick and Hugus.[6] To summarize, the relatively compact f orbitals can strengthen the bonds only if the oxygen atoms are quite close to the metal atom. In the linear dioxo-cation (oriented along, say, the z axis), the metal-oxygen bonds can be shortened by full use of both the p_x and p_y metal orbitals for a total of two π bonds. But in a symmetrical trioxo-cation (not known), for example, symmetry would permit a total of only *one* (say p_z) π bond distributed among the *three* metal-oxygen bonds.

We have examined the Lowry-Brønsted acidity, which refers to an already hydrated cation; we now consider the tendency toward *formation* of the same cation as a result of the *Lewis* acidity of the *unhydrated* ion. Again, the data[8] (free energies of hydration in Fig. 5–1) are incomplete and often doubtful, but patterns are evident, and some use will be made of them in the following chapters. Beside the familiar effects of charge and size, the influence of the additional polarizing strength of **d** ions is plain. For example, the crystal radius of Ag^+ is considerably larger than that of Na^+, yet the silver ion definitely has the

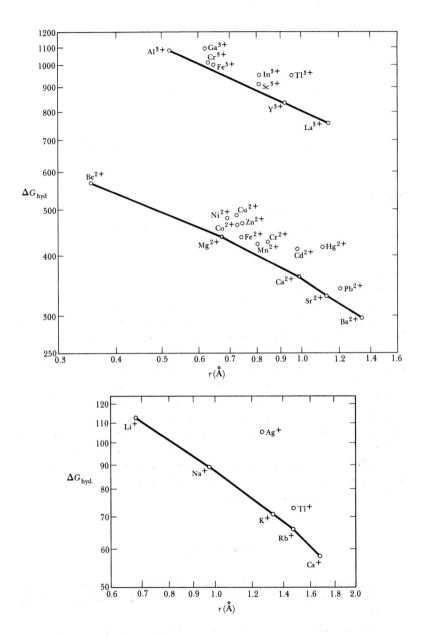

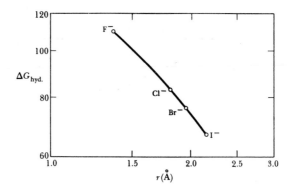

Fig. 5–1. Free energies of hydration of ions. Calculated from the list of J. P. Hunt, *Metal Ions in Solution* (New York: Benjamin, 1963), p. 16, but estimating entropies for Be^{2+}, Cr^{2+}, Sc^{3+}, Y^{3+} and Cr^{3+}.

larger tendency toward hydration. It is interesting to see, however, that the Lewis acidity of silver ion, according to this measure, is less than that of lithium ion, while in the case of the Brønsted acidity it is clearly the other way around. The apparently greater importance of polarizing strength in the Brønsted acidity can be understood by considering this acidity to result essentially from ability to hold in contact a single relatively polarizable hydroxide ion, while quantities such as enthalpy and free energy of hydration refer to interactions with less polarizable water molecules at various distances. Only the first sphere can be much affected by polarization and covalency, as opposed to electrostatic forces. Mercuric ion shows these differences even more sharply.

REFERENCES

1. R. P. Bell, *The Proton in Chemistry* (Ithaca, New York: Cornell, 1959), Chapter VII, "Acid-Base Strength and Molecular Structure."
2. J. C. McCoubrey, "The Acid Strength of the Hydrogen Halides," *Trans. Faraday Soc.* (1955), **51**, 743.
3. Chapter 1 of this book, references 23, 24, 28, and 32 on carbonyls and metallocene hydrides.

4. L. Pauling, *The Nature of the Chemical Bond* (3rd ed., Ithaca, New York: Cornell, 1960), p. 324, "The Strengths of the Oxygen Acids."

5. J. Bjerrum, G. Schwarzenbach, and L. G. Sillén, *Stability Constants, Inorganic Ligands, Special Pub. 7* (London: The Chemical Society, 1958), pp. 1–28, "Hydroxide."

6. R. E. Connick and Z. Z. Hugus, Jr., "The Participation of *f* Orbitals in Bonding in Uranium and the Transuranium Elements," *J. Am. Chem. Soc.* (1952), **74**, 6012. See also H. R. Hoekstra, *Inorg. Chem.* (1963), **2**, 492, supporting a U—O bond order greater than 2.

7. L. G. Sillén, "Quantitative Studies of Hydrolytic Equilibria," *Quart. Rev.* (1959), **13**, 146.

8. J. P. Hunt, *Metal Ions in Solution* (New York: Benjamin, 1963), p. 16, "Thermodynamic values for the hydration of gaseous ions at 25°C."

9. T. C. Waddington, *Adv. Inorg. Radiochem.* (New York: Academic Press, 1959), **1**: (in "Lattice Energies . . ."), p. 186, Fig. 1, "Enthalpies of hydration as functions of anion radii"; p. 187, Fig. 2, ". . . as functions of the lyotropic numbers of the anions."

10. A. F. Clifford, *Inorganic Chemistry of Qualitative Analysis* (Englewood Cliffs, New Jersey: Prentice-Hall, 1961), Sections 9–4 and 9–15 on "Electronegativity and Amphoterism."

11. *The Chemistry of the Coordination Compounds,* ed. J. C. Bailar, Jr. (New York: Reinhold, 1956), F. Basolo, Chapter 12, "Theories of Acids, Bases, Amphoteric Hydroxides and Basic Salts. . . ."

12. M. C. Day and J. Selbin, *Theoretical Inorganic Chemistry* (New York: Reinhold, 1962), Chapter 8, "Acids and Bases"; Selbin, "Metal Oxocations," *J. Chem. Ed.* (1964), **41**, 86.

13. R. M. Noyes, "Assignment of Individual Ionic Contributions to Properties of Aqueous Ions," *J. Am. Chem. Soc.* (1964), **86**, 971; R. H. Stokes, "The van der Waals Radii of Gaseous Ions of the Noble Gas Structure in Relation to Hydration Energies," *J. Am. Chem. Soc.* (1964), **86**, 979.

14. F. G. A. Stone, "Stability Relationships Among Analogous Molec-

The following references are some of the sources of quantitative and descriptive information used in this and the following chapters but hard or impossible to find in standard compilations: Reference 10, above (not only sections cited), numerous appendices and other tables.

ular Addition Compounds of Group III Elements," *Chem. Rev.* (1958), **58,** 101, including periodicity in Lewis acidity.

15. C. L. Chernick, "Chemical Compounds of the Noble Gases," *Record Chem. Prog.* (1963), **24,** 139.

16. *The Noble Gas Compounds,* ed. H. H. Hyman (Chicago: University of Chicago Press, 1963).

17. E. H. Appelman and J. G. Malm, ". . . the Aqueous Solution Chemistry of Xenon," *J. Am. Chem. Soc.* (1964), **86,** 2141; Appelman and Malm, "Characterization of Divalent Xenon in Aqueous Solution," *J. Am. Chem. Soc.* (1964), **86,** 2297.

18. A. Carrington and M. C. R. Symons, "Structure and Reactivity of the Oxyanions of Transition Metals," *Chem. Rev.* (1963), **63,** 443: Sections II and VI, ". . . Stability" and "Thermodynamic Properties . . ."; Sections III B, E, and F, and Table III, "Electronic Transitions . . ." and ". . . Spectra"; Section VIII, "Proton-Transfer Reactions"; Sections IX A and B, "Coordination of Solvent" and "Complex Formation. . . ."

19. G. Charlot, *L'Analyse Qualitative et les Réactions en Solution* (4th ed., Paris: Masson, 1957), Part II, "Propriétés chimiques et caractérisation des ions." (Table of contents after index.) Graphs of solubilities, oxidation states and electrode potentials versus pH; tables of equilibrium constants.

6

Oxidation State and
Redox Potential

6-1 GENERAL

Let us look again at the analysis of an electrochemical process into three steps using $1/8 \, S_8 + 2e^- \rightarrow S^{2-}(aq)$ as our present example: (1) atomization (vaporization and dissociation) of the solid sulfur, (2) the double ionization of the atoms by *acquisition* of electrons, and (3) the hydration of the gaseous ions. For metals, some parallelism among these steps can be seen in the fact that they all involve generally larger energies when there are larger valences. On the other hand, atomization of all elements (except the noble gases) requires energy, ionization requires energy (except for the halogens), and hydration of ions releases energy (in all cases). Entropy changes introduce further, usually smaller, complications. Moreover, the separate steps, as partly discussed earlier, are not simple themselves. Evidently, we should feel fortunate to find as much order as we do (below) in over-all redox processes.

There are several reasons for the present examination of periodicity in these rather complicated equilibria. One is their practical importance. Another is the absence of information on many of the separate steps, even where the net result is well known.

It has often been pointed out that oxidation states not known at all in water may be quite stable in other media or at different temperatures. However, the treatment of periodic trends here is limited to the better-known cases both by the availability of information and by the size of this book. And, of course, many of the basic factors would be unchanged, in other conditions, except for their relative weights.

Table 6–1 summarizes the facts[1-5] (see also Chapter 5, References 15–19) on stabilities of various oxidation states (involving coordination to only hydrogen or oxygen) in water containing H^+ and H_2 at unit activities. All potentials are referred consistently to the *element,* not to the various lower oxidation states. This removes unnecessary complications in comparing members of an isoelectronic series such as Au^+, Hg^{2+}, and Tl^{3+}, or in making comparisons within an isovalent series such as Sc^{3+}, Ti^{3+}, V^{3+}, and so on. This method of presentation does make less directly evident, of course, the trends for a series of elements going from, say, the 2+ to the 3+ state.

In the table, the oxidation states for each element decrease with complete regularity from the top down, including increasingly negative states below some elements. These are based on a universal assignment of 2− for coordinated oxygen and 1+ for hydrogen, regardless of electronegativity differences. This gives continuity to the hydride series, for example. Where an oxidation state is given without a potential, that state is known but usually quite unstable. Actual formulas are given if reasonably certain. Where catenation occurs, as in C_3H_8, S_4^{2-}, or even Hg_2^{2+}, P_2H_4 and N_2O, the nearly equal sharing of electrons causes the appearance of otherwise unusual oxidation states which do not adequately reflect the relatively simple electronic structures of the central atoms; such forms have therefore been omitted from the table. This can also be viewed as a strict interpretation of the rule for coordinating only O or H. It can be seen that there are still plenty of "odd" oxidation states left. In fact some, such as NO_2, are practically unique to oxides.

The superscripts show *net* ionic charges of the dominant species (per central atom if polynuclear), with acid-base equilibrium and unit activity of H^+. These data are included because comparisons of redox characteristics are best made in series showing net charges that are constant or changing uniformly. Some of the charges are quite dubious, however, and even a few probably wrong ones are included where the reported potential may depend on the investigator's assumptions. Since the net charges depend on the degree of hydrolysis or basicity, they can often be estimated (Sections 5–2 and 5–3).

Roman type represents ions or compounds that are stable against conversion to the free element by the H_2, H^+ couple. Plus and minus signs for the potentials are not used, because these would be opposite for positive and negative oxidation states. *Italic* type represents *unstable* ions or compounds.

Discussion of some individual examples may aid interpretation. Immediately below N, *1.87*$^+$ represents a unipositive ion having N in the $-I$ oxidation state, that is, NH_3OH^+ or hydroxylammonium ion. We see that this is unstable against oxidation by H^+ (or decomposition in this case) to elemental nitrogen: $NH_3OH^+ \rightarrow \frac{1}{2}N_2 + 2H^+ + H_2O + e^-$ or $NH_3OH^+ \rightarrow \frac{1}{2}N_2 + H^+ + H_2O + \frac{1}{2}H_2$. For the half reaction, the oxidation potential is $+ 1.87$ V, and the reduction potential and IUPAC electrode potential are $- 1.87$ V.

The fourth position (the only occupied one) above O stands for the formally $+IV$ oxidation state of oxygen as a central atom in "oxygen dioxide," that is, ozone. This completes the series that includes carbon(II) and nitrogen(III) (CO and HNO_2), which like many analogous series shows greater instability in the higher oxidation states. Incidentally, the ozone potential was of course calculated for the *four-electron* process $O_3 + 4H^+ + 4e^- \rightarrow \frac{1}{2}O_2 + 2H_2O$ using the standard free energies of ozone and water.

No potential is entered for AgO since this now appears to be $Ag^+AgO_2^-$. Conceivably, one or two actual entries could be invalidated in the same way.

In the sixth position above Mn we find .77 for Mn(VI) or manganate. In alkaline solution this is doubtless MnO_4^{2-}, and this is the formula usually given even in connection with its estimated potential in acid solution, but it should actually be similar to $HCrO_4^-$ or $Cr_2O_7^{2-}$.

In some cases we have more accurate potentials relating

Table 6-1 Redox Potentials

Hydrogen reference:

0.00^+	H
2.25^-	

Periodic arrangement of redox potentials:

Group IA	Group IIA				Transition elements								Group IIIB	Group IVB	Group VB	Group VIB	Group VIIB	0
Li 3.02^+	**Be** 1.85^{2+}												**B** 0.87^0	**C** 0.20^0	**N** 1.25^-, 1.37^0, 1.45^0, 1.68^0, 1.87^+	**O** 1.65^0	**F** 3.06^0	**Ne**
Na 2.71^+	**Mg** 2.37^{2+}												**Al** 1.66^{3+}	**Si** 0.7^0	**P** 0.51^0	**S**	**Cl** 1.63^0, 1.36^-	**Ar**
K 2.92^+	**Ca** 2.87^{2+}	**Sc** 2.08^{3+}	**Ti** 1.63^{2+}, 1.21^{3+}	**V** 1.18^{2+}, 0.87^{3+}, 0.25^+	**Cr** 0.91^{2+}, 0.74^{3+}, 0.42^{3+}	**Mn** 1.18^{2+}, 0.28^{3+}	**Fe** 0.44^{2+}, 0.04^{3+}	**Co** 0.28^{2+}, 0.42^{3+}	**Ni** 0.25^{2+}	**Cu** 0.34^{2+}, 0.52^+	**Zn** 0.76^{2+}		**Ga**	**Ge**	**As** 0.60^0, 0.36^0	**Se** 1.59	**Br** 1.07^-, 1.3^0	**Kr** 2.1^0

Additional couples and values noted about the table:

- 0.30^-, 0.74^-, 0.77, 1.08, (V), (III)
- 0.03^0, 0.53^0, 0.76^0
- 0.56^{3+}, 0.89^{2+}, 0.87^{3+}, 0.74^{3+}, 0.28^{3+}, 0.04^{3+}, 0.42^{3+}
- 1.63^{2+}, 1.18^{3+}, 0.91^{2+}, 1.18^{2+}, 0.44^{2+}, 0.28^{2+}, 0.25^{2+}, 0.34^{2+}, 0.76^{2+}, 0.52^+
- 1.05^0, 0.48^-, 1.1, 0.0^0, 0.46^0, 1.0, 1.1, $1.5?$
- 0.65^+, 0.1, 1.53^+, 0.28^0, 0.9, 1.3^0
- 2.37^{3+}, 1.13^+, 0.23^+, 0.83^{3+}, 1.6^+, 0.34^{3+}

Hydride species: BeH_4^{2-} (0.25^-), AlH_4^- (0.53^{3+}), GeH_4 (0.00, 0.21^+)

Chalcogen / halogen couples:
- O: 1.23^0, 0.36^-, 0.45^0
- S: 0.14^0, 0.88^0, 0.74^0
- F: 1.39^0, 1.47^-, 1.55^0, 1.64^0
- Cl: 1.52^-
- Se: 0.40^0, 0.69^0, 0.53^+
- Br: 1.20^0
- Kr: 1.8^0
- N: 0.27^+, 0.41^0, 0.50^0
- C: 0.33^+, 0.13^0, 0.86^0
- Si/Ge: 0.06^0, 0.37^0, 0.10^0, 0.1, 0.25^0, 0.0^0

	2.89^{2+}						0.45^{2+}	0.6^{2+}	0.99^{2+}		0.40^{2+}		0.14^{2+}				
2.99^{+}										0.80^{+}		In^{+}				1.45^{+}	
Rb	Sr	Y	Zr	Nb	Mo	Tc	Ru	Rh	Pd	Ag	Cd	In	Sn	Sb	Te	I	Xe
							0.85^{0}									0.54^{-}	
						0.37^{-}									0.72^{0}		
					0.09^{0}	0.31^{0}	(VI)	(VI)	(VI)					0.5^{0}	$0.9 ?^{0}$		
				0.81^{0}	0.10^{0}								SnH_4	0.8^{0}		1.4^{0}	
			1.70^{2+}		0.12^{0}	0.26^{0}		0.93^{0}	1.1^{0}				0.66^{0}		0.8^{0}		
		2.23^{2+}			0.11^{3+}			Ir^{3+}		1.50^{3+}		0.72^{3+}		0.32^{+}	0.6		
							0.8^{2+}		1.2^{2+}		0.85^{2+}		0.13^{2+}		0.6^{2+}		
										1.68^{+}		0.34^{+}				1.0	
		Lu	Hf	Ta	W	Re	Os	Ir	Pt	Au	Hg	Tl	Pb	Bi	Po	At	Rn
																0.3^{-}	
															PoH_2		
														BiH_3			
			1.42^{4+}	1.14^{4+}						Tb^{4+}			PbH_4				
		2.52^{3+}	2.48^{3+}	2.47^{3+}	2.44^{3+}	2.42^{3+}	2.41^{3+}	2.41^{3+}	2.40^{3+}	2.39^{3+}	2.35^{3+}	2.32^{3+}	2.30^{3+}	2.28^{3+}	2.27^{3+}	2.25^{3+}	
	2.90^{2+}						2.84^{2+}	3.40^{2+}						Tm^{2+}	2.83^{2+}		
3.02^{+}																	
Cs	Ba	La	Ce	Pr	Nd	Pm	Sm	Eu	Gd	Tb	Dy	Ho	Er	Tm	Yb	Lu	
					0.90^{2+}	0.58^{2+}	0.50^{2+}	0.33^{2+}									
				1.0^{+}	1.09^{+}	0.92^{+}	0.79^{+}	0.72^{+}									
			1.90^{4+}	1.2^{4+}	1.51^{4+}	1.33^{4+}	1.28^{4+}	1.16^{4+}		Bk^{4+}							
		2.6^{3+}			1.80^{3+}	1.83^{3+}	2.03^{3+}	2.36^{3+}	Cm^{3+}	Bk^{3+}	Cf^{3+}	Es^{3+}	Fm^{3+}	Md^{3+}	$^{3+}$	Lw^{3+}	
	2.92^{2+}																
Fr	Ra	Ac	Th	Pa	U	Np	Pu	Am	Cm	Bk	Cf	Es	Fm	Md		Lw	

one ion or compound to another than we have relating it to the element, although accuracy beyond two decimals is not needed here anyway. An extreme case, however, is the value for Bk^{3+}, Bk^{4+}, reported as 1.6 volts on the oxidizing side. Without any potential relating to the element, this information does not fit in our table.

With this background, what periodic trends can we see? The agreement of maximum and minimum oxidation state with number of "outer" electrons or vacancies in **s**, most **p**, early **d**, and very early **f**, elements is widely recognized even in elementary treatments of chemistry. We now have the question of why this does not hold for all elements. There are several contributing factors, some of them relatively speculative. All of these will now have our attention.

As ionization potentials show, the removal of each additional electron from an atom costs considerably more energy than that of the previous one, as expected for purely electrostatic reasons. This increasing cost, however, is increasingly compensated by the hydration energy of the aqueous ions (Section 5–3).

The hydration energy rises with charge, at first, for two reasons. One is that a larger charge interacts more strongly with a water molecule in a given orientation. The other is that a larger charge orients the water molecules more favorably. When the nearest water molecules are already fully oriented, the hydration energy can no longer rise so steeply. At about this point, hydrolysis becomes severe, yielding hydroxide ions (or, for anions, hydrogen ions), which are naturally attracted more strongly than are neutral molecules to the cations or anions under consideration. As cations with still greater charges again reach a kind of plateau in the ability of hydroxide ions to stabilize them, there is a further but final change of the coordinated group to the doubly negative oxide ion.

This whole process is one of the main factors accounting for a series like $Na(OH_2)_x{}^+$, $Mg(OH_2)_6{}^{2+}$, $Al(OH_2)_6{}^{3+}$, or $Al(OH_2)_5OH^{2+}$, $Si(OH)_4(?)$, $PO(OH)_3$, SO_3OH^-, $ClO_4{}^-$. The net stability falls rather regularly through some of these series, especially toward the end, in spite of some irregularities in net charge. Because no further stabilization by loss of H^+ can occur to compensate for additional energies of ionization, we are not surprised to see these series end fairly abruptly, for example, between ClO_4^- and nonexistent ArO_4, or after RuO_4. And, since fluoride ion cannot undergo similar changes, this, together with mild steric limitations on coordination number, is an important factor against the attainment of really high oxidation states with this ligand, even though F_2 is a powerful oxidant, notwithstanding that CoF_3 and AgF_2 represent, for these elements, *relatively* high states. For example OsF_8 (formerly reported but found to be OsF_6), and CrF_6 are not yet known, although ReF_7 and IF_7 are known, together with equivalent *oxygen*-coordinated ions or molecules in *all* these cases. It is especially interesting that XeO_6^{4-} has been prepared only through a fluoride (XeF_6, by disproportionation or ozonization in alkaline solution).

Extrapolation of this so far mainly electrostatic argument from fluorine back through oxygen to nitrogen would suggest the use of nitride ion to achieve high oxidation states for metal atoms. This fails, of course, because of the oxidizability of such a highly charged "anion" (but note the existence of OsO_3N^-). The same limitation also operates, even if less strongly, against oxides.

6-2   THE d AND f ELEMENTS

It remains to explain the particular points at which the series of maximum oxidation states end. In the **d** series these points are at MnO_4^-, RuO_4, and OsO_4. The **4d** and **5d** series go further than the **3d,** and the potentials show that the **5d** compounds are the most stable of all in the highest oxidation states. The greater size of the **4d** and **5d** atoms, and the resulting ease of loss of the last electrons (*but not the first*), may be at least part of the cause, although the ionization energies are not known for the last stages. There must be a considerable effect because the greater energies of atomization of the heavier elements have to be overcome. Possible explanations for the small difference between **4d** and **5d** seem even less satisfactory.

The early cutoff of the **4f** series at Ce^{4+} can be related to the fact (Fig. 1–3), that the f electrons become mostly unavailable fairly rapidly in these elements as atomic number and charge increase. In the same elements, the existence of Pr^{4+},

Sm^{2+}, and Tm^{2+} reminds us that the tendency toward empty, half-full, and full subshells is just that—a tendency only.

In some proposed forms of the periodic table, the importance of the half-full f subshell in the 4f elements is recognized more fully by a section of the table looking something like Fig. 6–1 as either a spiral or a helix.

The early 5f elements show much higher oxidation states than do the 4f types. This is one of the main evidences for the common idea that the f electrons in the former are less buried, more nearly equal in energy to the other valence electrons. And again, the 5f ions with a given charge are a bit larger, and this may facilitate the removal of further electrons. In any case, the effect seems to be enough to rule out Am^{2+}, even with a half-full subshell. It also makes uranium resemble tungsten more than it resembles neodymium. (But see p. 62 on Am.)

In the *late* d elements the maximum oxidation states have an irregularly decreasing pattern as we move to the right. This corresponds roughly to the decreasing availability of the d

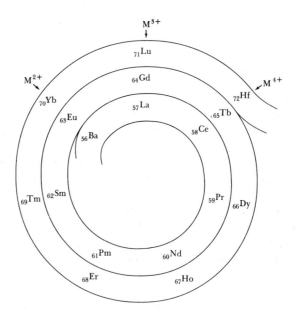

Fig. 6–1. Showing two periods in the rare earths and emphasizing oxidation states having empty, half-full, and full 4f subshells.

electrons in the valence shell. These transition elements, like the others mentioned previously, show a greater stability in the higher oxidation states as we pass down the columns of the periodic table. This is not always obvious from the numbers in Table 6–1. What we need to do is to look at the potentials between two of the common oxidation states, not including the free elements. As an example, the electrode potential for Pt(II)–Pt(IV) would be estimated from the table as $[4(1.1) - 2(1.2)]/2 = 1.0$ volts. The corresponding value for nickel is 1.77. Once more, the larger platinum atom seems to have the smaller final ionization energies (Chapter 1, Reference 1b).

In contrast, it is the *lighter* transition elements that are most stable in the lowest positive oxidation states. (But even continuing the exclusion of carbonyls and so on, rhenium, at least, has a "negative" oxidation state with hydride coordination. The formal oxidation state is not certain enough to go into the table.) This agrees with the fact that the potentials of these states include the energies of atomization, while the ordinary or stepwise potentials for further oxidation do not. As seen in Table 4–5, these energies are greatest at the bottom of the table, making it most difficult there to carry out the first steps in dissolution. This accentuates the effect of the greater first ionization energies of the heavy elements.

Carrying a given oxidation state across a row, we find a general decrease of stability toward the right. One of the most complete series is the one starting with Ca^{2+} and ending with Zn^{2+}. The striking trend in stability is again associated with the decreasing availability of all the electrons as the nuclear charge increases, and is in spite of partly contradictory trends in atomization energies and especially in hydration energies. The inordinately high stabilities of Ca^{2+}, Mn^{2+}, and Zn^{2+} are, of course, evidences of the tendency toward empty, half-full, and full subshells, as already seen in each of the component properties. In the **4d** and **5d** cases the tendency toward a half-full subshell does not appear. These larger atoms are known from spectral and magnetic data to pair their d electrons in most compounds. This results from the diminished interelectronic repulsions and deprives the half-full subshell of any special influence. In all of these series, however, there seem to be no convincing simple explanations for many of the missing oxidation states.

On the basis of all these considerations, we would expect some of the horizontal trends of the 4f elements. The potentials for Ba^{2+}, Sm^{2+}, and Yb^{2+} are unexpectedly close, however. This writer has no adequate explanation for the surprising fact that europium metal seems to be thermodynamically the strongest of all ordinary reducing agents (going to aqueous Eu^{2+}). The half-full subshell helps, but does not seem sufficient. Because the potential is not usually listed this way (at the very top of the emf series), the reader may wish to check the calculations, using data from any established compilation on the rare earths. (The Eu^{2+}, Eu^{3+} potential is given as 0.43 volts more reducing than H_2, H^+.)

With the 5f elements, the horizontal trend in the two highest oxidation states is toward lower stability to the right as expected. The 3+ state first becomes less stable toward further oxidation, with a tendency to lose all f electrons, then more stable as the f electrons become unavailable and perhaps as the energies of atomization fall with the metallic valence likely dropping to 3. The 4+ ions show a downward trend, but with a reversal at U^{4+}. Special stability is predictable here, at least if the ion is octahedral, on the basis of ligand-field theory. The f orbitals are split, with the f_{xyz} having its lobes pointing nicely between the ligands and having a uniquely low energy for two f electrons. This also appears in some of the properties of PuF_6, including the absence of temperature-dependent paramagnetism. The other six f orbitals are in two higher groups of three each.[25] This stabilization is not expected and not found in the linear MO_2^+ and MO_2^{2+} ions.

Before leaving the transition elements, it is useful to note that several oxidation states not listed, or listed as unstable, in Table 6–1 can be stabilized as chloro- and other complexes in aqueous solution. This is especially true with the middle and lower oxidation states of the heavy late **d** elements, including mainly the so-called platinum metals. While there is not space to discuss each ligand atom in detail here, a more general discussion appears in Chapter 8. The intimate connection between stability of a complex ion toward dissociation and its stability toward reduction allows us to cover the essential points in either context.

One apparent exception to the stability of 18-electron structures will be mentioned here, because it has puzzled some writers. The $Fe(CN)_6^{4-}$, $Fe(CN)_6^{3-}$ couple is *more* strongly reducing by

0.41 volts than the couple Fe^{2+}, Fe^{3+} in spite of the fact that the cyanoferrate(II) ion has an 18-electron or noble-gas structure. The puzzle probably results from neglect of the six additional negative charges in the cyano-complexes, compared to the aquo-ions; these would surely promote reducing character even more than observed, if no other influences were present.

6-3   THE s AND p ELEMENTS

Compared to the middle of the periodic table, the side regions reveal both old and new patterns. The most recurrent feature is of course the 8-electron shell. Once again the stabilities of positive oxidation states (as defined in Table 6–1) decrease toward the right as increasing nuclear charge makes valence electrons less removable. Extending this trend back toward the left, we find a sudden fall in stability of the unipositive ions of the d9 column. This cannot be due to low hydration energies, which are in fact rather high, compared to those of s cations of similar size and charge. Ionization energies do contribute something to the result, because the s valence electrons in these transition elements penetrate a sizeable d subshell, but this can explain reducibility only as compared to alkali-metal cations, not as compared to post-transition cations. The ionization energies in gold and mercury, however, are especially high and are an important part of their total behavior. With the lighter elements the remaining factor, the atomization energy, is dominant. This energy, as already noted, drops greatly from group d9 to group d10. In addition, this energy affects the electrode potential for bivalent and tervalent ions only a half or a third as much as for univalent ones, because the energy must be divided, so to speak, among all the valence electrons. This effect, particularly favoring the reducibility of univalent ions, is not overwhelming in the sl column, because they have roughly proportionately smaller energies of atomization, having no d electrons to participate in metallic bonding.

The stabilities of negative oxidation states, in the rows and columns taken separately, can be correlated qualitatively with the electronegativity of the atom in question, as is well known. Valid correlations of this sort can also be made with transition elements, but the changes of electronegativity there are not so striking.

There is further variety in the vertical trends. The increase of reducibility from Li^+ to Na^+ clearly can result only from the decrease of hydration energy for the larger ion. The trend elsewhere in the s columns is correspondingly due to the slight preeminence of the lower atomization and ionization energies of the larger atoms. While the direction of change of each of these three energies is as expected, there is no certain way we could have predicted which trend would be the strongest.

In the **p** columns, the pattern for positive oxidation states might at first sight appear nonexistent. Closer inspection brings out the strongly oxidizing character of the **2p** compounds (where, in fact, they exist at all) and the relatively very great stability toward reduction in the **3p** series. There is a clear alternation, particularly on the right side, ending in the strongly oxidizing nature of the **6p** row. This certainly does not agree well with the frequent statement that oxidizing ability increases from top to bottom, unless we ignore the first row completely and the slightly out-of-line character of the middle row. The latter statement is usually tied in with the so-called "inert pair" of s electrons, which is difficult to remove in changing Hg to Hg^{2+}, Tl^+ to Tl^{3+}, Pb^{2+} to PbO_2, BiO^+ to Bi_2O_5, and so on. We can see from Table 6–1, however, that the *lower* positive oxidation states, from approximately bismuth to the right, are also relatively hard to prepare.[6] In fact, radon, although giving rise to some fluoride chemistry, has not yet been found to have a solution chemistry, even in the presence of xenon carrier. The ability of the xenon, in a mixture with radon, to react with fluorine somewhat as usual, rules out the radiation as a sole source of instability. If we do use the inert-pair concept, it should be extended to some cases in the top and middle rows, such as the complete nonexistence of BrO_4^-.

Various explanations have been offered for this alternation.[7-12] One reason perfluorate is not known is that fluorine has no accessible d orbitals for d-p π bonding with oxygen, as has chlorine. Even in a (neutral) chlorine atom, the $3d$ orbitals would have rather high energy for bonding purposes. But in perchlorate ion the central atom carries some positive charge, and we know (Fig. 1–3) that such a charge lowers d energies relative to s and p. This effect of charge, which should strengthen the bonding, is supported by observations of decreasing Cl—O distances in the series: ClO_2^-, ClO_3^-, ClO_4^-, (1.57, 1.48, and 1.46 Å, respectively).

In the 4p series we might expect the same behavior. The $4d$ orbitals in hypothetical perbromate, however, would have a radial node about where the bonding electrons should be, thus greatly weakening any π bonds.[12] In contrast, BrO_3^-, like analogous ions, probably has in its favor that the lower formal charge on the central atom causes less contraction of the $4d$ orbital and permits the node to be beyond the main bonding region, although part of the orbital would be too far out for good overlap with the oxygen electrons. A further decrease of positive formal charge, as in GeO_3^{4-} (nonexistent but isoelectronic with BrO_3^-), may make the d orbitals so diffuse as to contribute negligibly, once again, to π bonding. Various other species seem fairly well covered by these and related arguments.

In periodate the bonding is less clear; the $5d$ orbitals may again be unimportant, although their two radial nodes could perhaps straddle the bonding region. Here, however, $4f$ orbitals should provide considerable bonding strength, much like that of the $3d$ in perchlorate. Finally, in hypothetical perastatate, the $5f$ orbitals have a radial node which may once more weaken the bonds.

Another feature in the oxidation states of the **p** elements is the absence, much more often than in the **d** and **f** elements, of odd states for even-numbered elements and vice versa. This reflects the familiar tendency toward having the p orbitals all full (therefore, no odd electrons) if any are occupied. This is more difficult for the **d** and **f** elements because the d and f orbitals are more numerous. Occupying them completely every time would mean larger coordination numbers, larger net charges, and a greater loss of "exchange energy" among the singly occupied orbitals.

By now the reader has probably noticed other patterns in this important part of chemistry, which has so often seemed chaotic. He will sharpen his understanding and enjoyment by testing the principles already discussed, and others, against the rich variety of facts provided by the generosity of nature.

6-4 TWO EXOTIC "ELEMENTS"

After this survey of the ordinary elements, the temptation is irresistible to include the few findings now available on the very interesting "element" positronium.[18] This, designated by Ps, is a combination of the positron with an electron and is really the zero nucleon or zero mass number isotope of hydrogen, $^0_1$H. The long-lived triplet form survives only 1.8×10^{-9} sec in H_2O, on the average, but evidence has been found for its ability to reduce Cu^{++}, $HgCl_2$, Sb(III), and Sn(IV), but not H_3O^+ or ions of cadmium or more electropositive metals. This is mostly as expected, although $Ps + H_3O^+ \rightarrow PsH_2O^+ + H$ ought to proceed because the binding energy of Ps is only half that of H, whose heavy nucleus has negligible kinetic energy. The energies of the ions should probably not cancel this effect, at least thermodynamically.

This is significant work in chemistry by physicists, although neglect of activation energies and of the complex nature of tin and antimony in these solutions plus the irrelevance of the electrode potential involving Hg_2Cl_2 at such low concentrations weaken or invalidate some of the conclusions.

If we now really stretch our definitions, we can regard the hydrated electron as a hydrated anion of the "element" having both zero mass number and zero nuclear charge—the light isotope of the neutron! The electron in aqueous solution is also comparable to free radicals such as the hydrogen atom. Where only one electron is required, both are strong reducing agents, having no covalent bonds of their own to break, but the hydrated electron also has no proton of its own to hold it back; it can, as expected, rapidly reduce things that even hydrogen atoms cannot—$Co(NH_3)_6{}^{3+}$, Pb^{2+}, Cd^{2+}, Ni^{2+}, Co^{2+}, Cr^{3+}, Zn^{2+}—in the approximate order of decreasing reactivity, in addition to Fe^{3+}, Cu^{2+}, and Ag^+, which are also rapidly reduced by H atoms.[19-20] Comparison with the order of electrode potentials for these ions shows perhaps an even better correlation than might be expected, considering the several factors involved. It has also been found that the tervalent rare-earth ions have an excellent correlation between their reactivities with the hydrated electron[22] and the stabilities of the resulting bivalent ions. Here the order of reactivity is: $Eu^{3+} > Yb^{3+} > Sm^{3+} > Tm^{3+} >$ others.

6-5 REDOX KINETICS

A separate chapter on periodicity in kinetics is outside the scope of this work, but a few patterns in redox processes stand out rather clearly. Consider a number of examples involving **p** elements: Perchlorate and periodate are both good oxidizing agents thermodynamically, but the latter is ordinarily much faster. Silane and phosphine take fire in air extremely easily, while methane and ammonia, also strong reducing agents, are much more inert. H_2O_2 can be preserved much longer at ordinary conditions than H_2S_2, although the self-reduction-oxidation of the latter is less energetic. The atmosphere contains large quantities of oxygen (O—O bonds) in spite of the presence of good reducing agents in and on the earth's crust; in contrast, the system RS—$SR + 2\,H^+ + 2\,e^- = 2\,RS$—$H$ is the basis of some very effective biological catalysts.

In the previous examples and many more we observe that elements below the **2p** row generally react much faster than their lighter congeners. This extends even to many, but not all, organic substitution reactions involving the halogens. Fluorine is sometimes exceptional, however, for example in the violent reactions of F_2.

One of the reasons for the usual behavior may be the availability of empty outer d orbitals in the heavier atoms. These can strengthen the bonding in certain activated complexes. Also, the larger size provides both greater polarization forces and greater exposure of the surface to attack. Further analysis requires a study of mechanisms, which is treated by Edwards (Chapter 8, Reference 11).

REFERENCES

1. W. M. Latimer, *Oxidation Potentials* (2nd ed., Englewood Cliffs, New Jersey: Prentice-Hall, 1952).
2. G. Charlot, D. Bézier and J. Courtot, *Constantes Sélectionnées, Potentiels d'oxydo-réduction* (London: Pergamon, 1958).
3. R. Parsons, *Handbook of Electrochemical Constants* (London: Butterworths, 1959).
4. G. Milazzo, *Electrochemistry*, trans. P. J. Mill (Amsterdam: Elsevier, 1963), pp. 156–172, tables of "Series of Electric Tensions."
5. L. B. Asprey and B. B. Cunningham, "Unusual Oxidation States of Some Actinide and Lanthanide Elements," *Prog. Inorg. Chem.* (New York: Interscience, 1960), **2**, 267.
6. R. S. Drago, "Thermodynamic Evaluation of the Inert Pair Effect," *J. Phys. Chem.* (1958), **62**, 353.

7. Z. Z. Hugus, Jr., "The Possible Use of 4*f* Orbitals in Bonding: the Enhanced Stability of the Higher Oxidation States of Iodine, Tellurium and Antimony; the Non-existence of Perbromic Acid," *J. Am. Chem. Soc.* (1952), **74**, 1076.

8. D. W. J. Cruickshank, "The Role of 3*d*-Orbitals in π-Bonds between (a) Silicon, Phosphorus, Sulphur, or Chlorine and (b) Oxygen or Nitrogen," *J. Chem. Soc.* (1961), 5486, including, facing p. 5487, a photograph of a model.

9. A. F. Clifford, *Inorganic Chemistry of Qualitative Analysis* (Englewood Cliffs, New Jersey: Prentice-Hall, 1961), Chapter 16, "Apparent Anomalies in the Periodic Table."

10. G. W. Chantry and R. A. Plane, "Raman Intensities and the Structure of Some Oxyanions of Group VII," *J. Chem. Phys.* (1961), **34**, 1268.

11. W. E. Dasent, "Non-existent Compounds," *J. Chem. Ed.* (1963), **40**, 130.

12. D. S. Urch, "The Perbromate Problem," *J. Inorg. Nuc. Chem.* (1963), **25**, 771.

13. J. Kleinberg, *Unfamiliar Oxidation States and Their Stabilization* (Lawrence: University of Kansas, 1950).

14. *The Chemistry of the Coordination Compounds,* ed. J. C. Bailar, Jr. (New York: Reinhold, 1956), J. V. Quagliano and R. L. Rebertus, Chapter 11, "Stabilization of Valence States Through Coordination."

15. (a) J. Chatt, "The stabilization of low valent states of the transition metals." *J. Inorg. Nuc. Chem.* (1958), **8**, 515. (b) W. Klemm, "Die Stabilisierung hoher Valenzstufen," *J. Inorg. Nuc. Chem.* (1958), **8**, 532.

16. R. S. Nyholm and M. L. Tobe, "The Stabilization of Oxidation States of the Transition Metals," *Adv. Inorg. Radiochem.* (New York: Academic Press, 1963), **5**, 1.

17. P. Delahay, M. Pourbaix and P. van Rysselberghe, "Potential-pH Diagrams," *J. Chem. Ed.* (1950), **27**, 683.

18. J. D. McGervey, H. Horstman, and S. DeBenedetti, "Mean Lives of Positrons in Oxidizing Solutions," *Phys. Rev.* (1961), **124**, 1113. Also (too recent to consider in Section 6–4) J. Green and J. Lee, *Positronium Chemistry* (New York: Academic Press, 1964).

19. J. H. Baxendale *et al., Proc. Chem. Soc.* (1963), 148, 241, and 242; M. Anbar and D. Meyerstein, *Proc. Chem. Soc.* (1964), 23: all on the hydrated electron.

20. M. S. Matheson, W. A. Mulac, and J. Rabani, "Formation of the Hydrated Electron in the Flash Photolysis . . . ," *J. Phys. Chem.* (1963), **67**, 2613.

21. *Disc. Faraday Soc.,* "Fundamental Processes in Radiation Chemistry" (1963), No. 36, by various authors, especially pp. 193 and 214; see earlier references there. Also, J. H. Baxendale, "Addendum: Redox Potential and Hydration Energy of the Hydrated Electron," *Radiation Res.* (1964), Suppl. 4, p. 139; $E° = 2.7$ V, and $\Delta G_{hyd} = -40$ kcal/mole.

22. J. K. Thomas, S. Gordon, and E. J. Hart, "The Rates of Reaction of the Hydrated Electron in Aqueous Inorganic Solutions," *J. Phys. Chem.* (1964), **68**, 1524.

23. F. C. Anson, "Electrode Sign Conventions," *J. Chem. Ed.* (1959), **36**, 394, on the confusion particularly surrounding the so-called American convention.

24. L. B. Asprey and B. B. Cunningham, "Unusual Oxidation States of Some Actinide and Lanthanide Elements," *Prog. Inorg. Chem.* (New York: Interscience, 1960), **2**, 267.

25. H. G. Friedman, Jr., G. R. Choppin, and D. G. Feuerbacher; also C. Becker: *J. Chem. Ed.* (1964), **41**, 354 and 358: both on the geometry of *f* orbitals. And see I. Cohen, "The Shape of $2p$ and Related Orbitals," *J. Chem. Ed.* (1961), **38**, 20, correcting the common confusion of angular wave functions with orbital shapes. R. B. Leighton, *Principles of Modern Physics* (New York: McGraw-Hill, 1959), pp. 178–179, shows electron clouds for various kinds of *s, p, d,* and *f* orbitals.

26. R. Ferreira, *Inorg. Chem.* (1964), **3**, 1803, makes and justifies predictions for argon compounds.

7

Color and Redox Reactivity

7-1 INTRODUCTION

We noted in Section 4–1 that high electronic polarizability and refraction of light require some of the occupied and unoccupied orbitals (of appropriately different symmetries) to be close to each other in energy. Clearly the ability to absorb light has some of the same requirements. Just as with polarizability, then, color indicates an electronic responsiveness usually associated with either oxidizability or reducibility. One reason for emphasizing visible light here is that the data available are amenable to a fuller discussion of periodicity. Another is that infrared transitions are not usually electronic, while those in the ultraviolet, being more energetic and therefore more universal, tell less about gross *differences* in reactivity.

Some of the complications in the relation of color to reactivity are: (1) chemical reactions often involve more than one electron at a time; (2) optical transitions, unlike redox reactions, are too fast for simultaneous atomic rearrangements (Franck-Condon principle); (3) optical excitations, like internal decompositions (PtF_6), but unlike reactions with external reagents

$(Pr^{3+} \rightarrow Pr^{4+})$, may involve no change in charge or energy of hydration, and so on. Nevertheless, the considerable chemical information revealed by periodicity in color may have been undervalued by students with a strong interest in the sophisticated tools of modern spectroscopy. The valuable insights, especially into structure, attainable by detailed study of spectral curves are given by others.

7-2 ELEMENTS

The relation between color and reactivity is perhaps clearest in various types of compounds, but it is appropriate first, to give brief attention to the colors of elements. In this small class of substances, most of the members are metals and do not show much periodicity in color. Table 7–1 therefore lists the colors of the nonmetals.

We do find some correlation with reactivity even here; thus, the noble gases are colorless. In the other columns, the heaviest elements are the ones that absorb light at the lowest wavelengths and they are also the ones that, although least easily reduced, are most easily oxidized. This is reasonable because the absorption of light in these cases (for example, Br_2) partially removes an electron from a bonding to an antibonding molecular orbital farther

Table 7-1   Colors of Nonmetals

			H_2 colorless	He colorless
C_∞, C_∞ colorless, black	N_2 colorless	O_2, O_3 pale blue	F_2 pale yellow	Ne colorless
	P_4, P_∞, P_∞ white, red, black	S_8 yellow	Cl_2 yellow-green	Ar colorless
		Se_8, Se_∞ red, gray	Br_2 red-brown	Kr colorless
		$I_2, (I_2)_\infty$ violet, black	Xe colorless
				Rn colorless

from the nuclei. The antibonding feature is related to molecular dissociation, as in the photo-induced reactions of chlorine or bromine with hydrogen or hydrocarbons.

A factor causing the greater *intensity* of color in the heavier elements is the larger size of their molecules, This effect is seen in all kinds of wave motion. Both sound waves and water waves bypass objects much smaller than their wavelengths, but are stopped by larger ones. Even with a given element, we find that the allotrope having larger molecules is more intensely colored, except in the case of diamond and graphite. The formula $(I_2)\infty$, incidentally, is meant to show that solid iodine has its atoms paired, but with some covalent or metallic bonding between pairs, as suggested by its metallic luster. Organic dyes also illustrate the connection between molecular size and color.

7-3   BINARY COMPOUNDS

Table 7–2 lists oxides, sulfides, and iodides of most of the cations with s^2p^6, d^{10}, and f^{14} structures. Except as discussed below, absorption of light by these compounds causes partial transfer of an electron ("charge transfer") from "anion" to "cation." Therefore, sulfides (containing the more oxidizable anion) are almost always at least as dark as the analogous oxides.

Because iodides are included to represent the oxidizable end of the halogen series, and because fluoride ion, on the other end, is the least oxidizable of all simple ions, it would be logical to list the fluorides for contrast. These are omitted, however, precisely because of their colorlessness. The only definitely known exceptions in which the cations have the complete subshell structures of Table 7–2 appear to be the pale yellow ReF_7 and the yellow AgF. Fluorides of **p** elements with only *s* subshells intact are also generally colorless, for example, NF_3, BrF_5, TlF, and XeF_6 (the last as the solid at room temperature). We conclude that visible light is not able to transfer charge from F^- even with the help of oxidants like Bi^{5+}. This stability of fluoride, then, in contrast to iodide, sulfide, or even oxide, makes sense of many observations of color. On the other hand, AgF is yellow and out of line with the well-known white AgCl. (CuF and AuF are nonexistent or very poorly characterized.) Here we have to invoke interactions among the metal atoms, which the few small fluoride ions do not keep far apart. Processes similar to

$2Ag^+ \rightarrow Ag + Ag^{2+}$ may occur. Replacement of two fluoride ions by just one oxide ion should facilitate such interactions. The oxides in this part of the periodic table, in fact, do show some dark colors, and this is less evident to the right where the oxide ions separating the metal atoms become more numerous. As expected, the iodides, containing the largest and most numerous anions, do not show a darkening on the left side of the series.

Having examined mainly the effect of the anion, we now give further attention to the cations. The compounds of the s elements are not tabulated because they are all white except K_2O, Rb_2O, and Cs_2O, which are yellowish to orange, darkening greatly at higher temperatures. These colors can hardly represent cation-cation interactions because heating causes *expansion* of the lattice, and because the cations, unlike the d and p types, do not have variable valence and are the weakest polarizers possible among simple cations. Cs_2O, which is almost black at 250°, has the antifluorite structure with alternate octahedral anion positions vacant. This suggests the presence of the so-called F-centers (Farbe, or color) arising from the thermal transfer of one electron from an oxide ion to an adjacent vacancy, where energy levels are close enough together for absorption of light. We recall from our study of ionization potentials that the isolated oxide ion is unstable; the second "extra" electron is, of course, retained best near small highly charged cations.

With the exceptions mentioned in the two preceding paragraphs, the cations having the largest charges in a row are the best color producers, just as they are the best oxidants. In the columns, too, the strongest oxidants have the darkest colors. As an example of both these statements, compare, say, CrO_3 (the most reactive of these three) with TiO_2 and WO_3. In the d columns the largest oxidation potentials and the most pronounced colors are found at the top; in the p columns, it is, if anything, the other way around, with some tendency toward alternation, as seen in Chapter 6. In fact, some of the gaps in the table reflect extreme cases of the general redox instability of compounds in those regions. Illustrations are Mn_2S_7 (nonexistent) or TlI_3 ($Tl^+I_3^-$ exists but does not have the structure [Tl^{3+}, $3I^-$] of interest here). Even some of the sulfides included may be like TlI_3 in having deceptive formulas. However, the late p elements show much less color than the late d, as in Cl_2O_7 versus Mn_2O_7. This can be interpreted partly in terms of the greater tendency of the

Table 7-2 *Colors* of Some Binary Compounds*

	Group 3	Group 4	Group 5	Group 6	Group 7	Group 8		Group 11	Group 12	Group 13	Group 14	Group 15	Group 16	Group 17
Period 2										B_2O_3 w $\;$ B_2S_3 w $\;$ BI_3 w	CO_2 c $\;$ CS_2 c $\;$ CI_4 rd	N_2O_5 w		
Period 3										Al_2O_3 w $\;$ Al_2S_3 w $\;$ Al_2I_6 w	SiO_2 w $\;$ SiS_2 w $\;$ SiI_4 w	P_4O_{10} w $\;$ P_4S_{10} yl	SO_3 w	Cl_2O_7 c
Period 4	Sc_2O_3 w $\;$ Sc_2S_3 yl	TiO_2 w $\;$ TiS_2 yl $\;$ TiI_4 r–b	V_2O_5 or	CrO_3 d dr	Mn_2O_7 d gn			Cu_2O rd $\;$ Cu_2S bk $\;$ CuI w	ZnO w $\;$ ZnS w $\;$ ZnI_2 yl	Ga_2O_3 w $\;$ Ga_2S_3 w,yl $\;$ GaI_3 w	GeO_2 w $\;$ GeS_2 w $\;$ GeI_4 or	As_2O_5 w $\;$ As_2S_5 yl	SeO_3 w	
Period 5	Y_2O_3 w $\;$ Y_2S_3 yl	ZrO_2 w $\;$ ZrI_4 yl	Nb_2O_5 w	MoO_3 w $\;$ MoS_3 r–b	Tc_2O_7 yl $\;$ Tc_2S_7 d br	RuO_4 yl		Ag_2O bk $\;$ Ag_2S bk $\;$ AgI yl	CdO br $\;$ CdS yl $\;$ CdI_2 br	In_2O_3 yl $\;$ In_2S_3 yl,rd $\;$ InI_3 yl,rd	SnO_2 w $\;$ SnS_2 yl $\;$ SnI_4 yl	Sb_2O_5 l yl $\;$ Sb_2S_5 or	TeO_3 w	$XeO_4 \rightarrow$ l yl

La$_2$O$_3$ w	CeO$_2$ w	
La$_2$S$_3$ yl		

Lu$_2$O$_3$	HfO$_2$	Ta$_2$O$_5$	WO$_3$	Re$_2$O$_7$	OsO$_4$	Au$_2$O	HgO	Tl$_2$O$_3$	PbO$_2$	Bi$_2$O$_5$
w	w	w	yl	yl	l yl	d	rd,yl	d br	br	r–b
			WS$_3$	Re$_2$S$_7$		Au$_2$S	HgS	Tl$_2$S$_3$		
			d br	bk		d br	rd,bk	d bu		
		TaI$_5$				AuI	HgI$_2$			
		d br				yl	rd			

Ac$_2$O$_3$	ThO$_2$	Pa$_2$O$_5$	UO$_3$
w	w	w	or
Ac$_2$S$_3$	ThS$_2$		
d	d		
AcI$_3$	ThI$_4$		
w	w		

*Abbreviations for Tables 7–2 and 7–3:

,	or		vt	violet
w	white		pp	purple
c	colorless		pk	pink
f	faint		br	brown
l	light or pale		bk	black
d	dark		y-g	yellow-green
rd	red		b-g	blue-green
or	orange		r-b	red-brown
yl	yellow		b-v	blue-violet
gn	green		y-b	yellow-brown
bu	blue		r-v	red-violet

latter types to undergo one-electron, rather than two-electron, changes. (See Section 7–1 and Table 6–1.)

Most of the anhydrous oxides, sulfides, and halides of elements with incomplete d subshells, for example, NiS, are dark colored or even black. Strong metal-metal interactions in the oxides and sulfides, whose lower valences correspond to higher cation to anion ratios than many of the entries in Table 7–2, are indicated by moderate electrical conductivity, ferromagnetism or antiferromagnetism, and metallic luster in some cases. The fluorides, more ionic, often have lighter and brighter colors as do some compounds of Mn^{2+} and Fe^{3+}, whose d subshells are exactly half full and relatively stable against interactions.

To observe colors free from such interactions it is necessary to have the **d** metal atoms more widely separated, as in hydrated or other mononuclear complex ions. Most binary compounds of tervalent **f** elements, however, have about the same colors as the aqueous ions. This reflects good shielding of the f electrons from the chemical environment by the outer electrons.

7-4 COMPLEXES

Table 7–3 presents the colors of hydrated cations and some other derivatives of **d** and **f** elements. The sequences given are selected for being relatively complete in each series. The hydrated cations are given as examples of low polarization and covalency with the cyanide complexes representing the other extreme. However, the colors of reducible ions like Ce^{4+} and UO_2^{2+} represent some polarization because anhydrous CeF_4 and UF_6 are colorless. In fact, the ability of light to complete the transfer of electrons to the cations has practical use in the uranyl oxalate actinometer and in the proposed harnessing of sunlight for power production, involving generation of oxygen from solutions of Ce^{4+} in one of the steps.

The sandwich compounds, or cyclopentadienides, are included because of the bearing their colors have on the fascinating structural questions they raise. In the series derived from the strongly polarizing tervalent metal ions, there is no relationship of color to that of the cyano- or aquo-complexes except that $CoCpd_2^+$ and $Co(CN)_6^{3-}$ are both yellow (requiring absorption of energetic violet light) like so many other complexes of **d** elements having no unpaired electrons, fairly small ligands, and large ligand-field splittings of the d energy levels.

Hydration of the sandwich compound cations with incomplete lower d (t_{2g}) orbitals (accepting electron density from H_2O) doubtless affects their colors. Coordination of water to the metal atom is geometrically possible and solutions of even the neutral compounds $CrCpd_2$ and $MnCpd_2$ in the basic solvent tetrahydrofuran, but not in nonbasic petroleum ether, have colors (reported as bluish-red and yellow-amber, respectively) different from those in Table 7–3 for nonsolvated substances. (See Chapter 1, Reference 24, for these colors.)

In the several series derived from the bivalent and therefore only moderately polarizing metal ions, both the color and the number of unpaired electrons relate $MnCpd_2$ (the pink form) to Mn^{2+}, $NiCpd_2$ to Ni^{2+}, *but* $CrCpd_2$ to $Cr(CN)_6^{4-}$ and $FeCpd_2$ to $Fe(CN)_6^{4-}$. From these observations alone we can guess that the ligand-field strength of cyclopentadienide ion is somewhat less than that of cyanide ion but more than that of water. If it were closer to that of water we might expect $CrCpd_2$ to be blue while $FeCpd_2$, having a configuration with the low-energy t_{2g} orbitals just full, would more easily remain orange. And tetrahydrofuran (which, like water, coordinates through oxygen) does not, in fact, appear to affect ferrocene as it does chromocene. The bluishness of chromocene in this solvent suggests that some of the molecules are in a solvated and more ionic form. Many of the colors of these variable-valence substances having incomplete d subshells are due, as discussed by others, to d-d rather than charge-transfer processes.

When $MnCpd_2$ is in liquid form or solid solution with $MgCpd_2$, it is pink and paramagnetic in accord with the extra stability of the half-full subshell; in the pure solid at room temperature, it is brown and antiferromagnetic, showing interaction among the molecules. The difference between the pink manganese compound, with five unpaired electrons, and the iron compound, with zero rather than four, is of course not accounted for by any diagram like Fig. 1–2 which deals with isolated atoms. Still, we might have thought that if the effect of the ligand is enough to pair all the iron electrons, it would be enough to pair all but one of the manganese electrons. Actually, among five electrons with the same spin, there are $5!/(5-2)!2! = 10$ combinations taken two at a time in which the Pauli principle reduces mutual approach and electrostatic repulsion energy (Chapter 1, Reference 11a). The sixth electron in high-spin iron(II), however, adds five combinations with opposite spin that work the

Table 7-3 *Colors* of Some Complexes*

	0	1	2	3	4	5	6	7	8	9	10
number of d electrons	0	1	2	3	4	5	6	7	8	9	10
hydrated	Ca²⁺ c 0			V²⁺ vt 3	Cr²⁺ bu 4	Mn²⁺ f pk 5	Fe²⁺ l gn 4	Co²⁺ pk 3	Ni²⁺ gn 2	Cu²⁺ b-g 1	Zn²⁺ c 0
number of unpaired electrons	CaCpd₂ w 0		TiCpd₂ gn 0	VCpd₂ vt 3	CrCpd₂ rd 2	MnCpd₂ pk,br 5,af	FeCpd₂ or 0	CoCpd₂ vt 1	NiCpd₂ gn 2		ZnCpd₂ w 0
				VCy₆⁴⁻ y-b 3	CrCy₆⁴⁻ rd 2	MnCy₆⁴⁻ bu 1	FeCy₆⁴⁻ l yl 0		NiCy₄²⁻ yl 0	CuCy₄²⁻ pp 1 ?	ZnCy₄²⁻ c 0
octahedral	KCaF₃ w				KCrF₃ l bu	KMnF₃ w	KFeF₃ w	KCoF₃ pk	KNiF₃ l yl	KCuF₃ w	KZnF₃ w
	ScF₆³⁻ c 0	TiF₆³⁻ l vt 1	VF₆³⁻ gn 2	CrF₆³⁻ gn 3	MnF₆³⁻ b-v 4	FeF₆³⁻ c	CoF₆³⁻ l bu 4	NiF₆³⁻ vt	CuF₆³⁻ l gn 2		GaF₆³⁻ c 0
						MnCl₄²⁻ c	FeCl₄²⁻ c	CoCl₄²⁻ bu	NiCl₄²⁻ bu	CuCl₄²⁻ yl	ZnCl₄²⁻ c
hydrated	Sc³⁺ c 0	Ti³⁺ pp 1	V³⁺ gn 2	Cr³⁺ vt 3	Mn³⁺ vt 4	Fe³⁺ f vt 5	Co³⁺ bu				Ga³⁺ c 0
hydrated?	TiCpd₂⁺ gn 1		VCpd₂⁺ vt 2	CrCpd₂⁺ gn 3		FeCpd₂⁺ bu 1	CoCpd₂⁺ yl 0	NiCpd₂⁺ yl 1			
		TiCy₆³⁻ bu	VCy₆³⁻ y-b	CrCy₆³⁻ l yl 3	MnCy₆³⁻ yl, d rd 2	FeCy₆³⁻ yl,rd 1	CoCy₆³⁻ f yl 0				

number of *f* electrons	0	1	2	3	4	5	6	7	8	9	10	11	12	13	14
				ReF_6^{2-} c	OsF_6^{2-} f yl	IrF_6^{2-} l yl, pk	PtF_6^{2-} yl								PbF_6^{2-} w (s)
				$ReCl_6^{2-}$ y–g	$OsCl_6^{2-}$ or	$IrCl_6^{2-}$ or	$PtCl_6^{2-}$ yl								$PbCl_6^{2-}$ yl
	HfF_6^{2-} c			$ReBr_6^{2-}$ yl	$OsBr_6^{2-}$ d pp	$IrBr_6^{2-}$ bu	$PtBr_6^{2-}$ or								
				ReI_6^{2-} d vt	OsI_6^{2-} vt		PtI_6^{2-} d br (s)								
number of unpaired electrons	0	1	2	3	4	5	6	7	6	5	4	3	2	1	0
	Ba^{2+} c														
	La^{3+} c	Ce^{3+} c	Pr^{3+} y–g	Nd^{3+} r–v	Pm^{3+} rd	Sm^{3+} yl	Eu^{3+} f pk	Gd^{3+} c	Tb^{3+} f pk	Dy^{3+} l y–g	Ho^{3+} br	Er^{3+} rd	Tm^{3+} gn	Yb^{3+} c	Lu^{3+} c
							Sm^{2+} rd	Eu^{2+} yl						Tm^{2+} pp	Yb^{2+} gn
	Ac^{3+} c			U^{3+} rd	Np^{3+} pp	Pu^{3+} bu	Am^{3+} l pk	Cm^{3+} c	Bk^{3+} f,c?	Cf^{3+} f,c?					
	Th^{4+} c	Pa^{4+} c	U^{4+} gn	Np^{4+} y–g	Pu^{4+} br			Bk^{4+} c							
	PaO_2^+ c	UO_2^+ pk	NpO_2^+ gn	PuO_2^+ r–v	AmO_2^+ yl										
	UO_2^{2+} yl	NpO_2^{2+} pk	PuO_2^{2+} yl-or	AmO_2^{2+} br											

Cy_n = $(CN)_n$
Cpd = cyclopentadienyl = C_5H_5
af = antiferromagnetic
(s) = in a solid salt

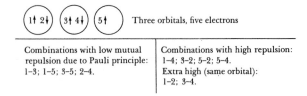

Combinations with low mutual repulsion due to Pauli principle: 1–3; 1–5; 3–5; 2–4.

Combinations with high repulsion: 1–4; 3–2; 5–2; 5–4.
Extra high (same orbital): 1–2; 3–4.

Fig. 7–1. An example of the effect of the Pauli principle on interelectronic repulsions and pairing.

other way. Similarly, in low-spin Mn(II) we have a total of four favorable and six unfavorable combinations (Fig. 7–1), while low-spin Fe(II) gives six favorable and nine unfavorable ones. Pairing would therefore raise interelectronic energies in six out of 10 of the combinations for manganese but only in four out of 15 for iron. Allowing for the extra large effect *within* a given orbital (compared to that between two different ones) does not change the net result because two additional orbitals in both atoms are completely filled by pairing.

Similar interactions can account for the redness of solid $K_3Mn(CN)_6$ and $K_3Fe(CN)_6$ in contrast to the yellow colors of dilute solutions. All of these systems (still including $MnCpd_2$) have π electrons similar to those in conjugated chains and in electrical conductors like graphite. The tervalent cyano-complex ions are more subject than the quadrivalent ones $[M(CN)_6^{4-}]$ to such effects, probably because of the greater covalency in the former and the greater number of interspersed cations in the latter. In the light-colored $Cr(CN)_6^{3-}$ and $Co(CN)_6^{3-}$, the t_{2g} orbitals are exactly half full, and full, respectively, as they generally are also in the lighter-colored halide complexes, included here for $5d(IV)$ ions in solution. The much deeper color of $Cr(H_2O)_6^{3+}$ is, of course, related to the lower ligand-field strength of H_2O, compared to that of CN^-. The deep colors of complexes with the heavy halogens correlate with the oxidizability of the halide ions. It can be noted here that with polyatomic ligands whose coordinated atoms have no multiple bonding, the other atoms hardly affect the color of the complex. Complexes with polyphosphates and oxalate, for example, look about the same as the hydrated ions. Isomerism, contrarily, *is* important, as shown by cis- (purple) and trans- (green) $CoEn_2Cl_2^+$.

Among the rare earths, the colors of the ions show some

similarity to each other at positions equidistant from the center of the series. In some periodic charts this relationship is represented as follows (but see Fig. 6–1):

$$_{57}La \quad _{58}Ce \quad _{59}Pr \quad _{60}Nd \quad _{61}Pm \quad _{62}Sm \quad _{63}Eu$$
$$_{71}Lu \quad _{70}Yb \quad _{69}Tm \quad _{68}Er \quad _{67}Ho \quad _{66}Dy \quad _{65}Tb \qquad _{64}Gd$$

This suggests a partial correspondence, expected theoretically, between energy levels for the configurations f^n and f^{14-n}. The latter has as many orbital vacancies as the former has electrons. Both have the same values for the spin vector S and the orbital vector L. All of these tervalent ions have quite pale colors, compared to Br_2 or MnO_4^-, for instance, since the symmetry of the f-f transitions involved in incomplete subshells "forbids" dipole radiation or absorption. The sharpness of the absorption bands indicates the absence of interaction with the environment. The colorlessness of those ions having empty, half-full, or full subshells is another indication of their redox stability. Charge again affects color greatly, however. The colors of the oxidizable bivalent 4f ions are associated with either their easy loss of a third electron even to water molecules or at least their easy excitation of the electron to perhaps $5d$ or $5g$ orbitals. The absorption bands are broad, showing environmental influences.

The lack of chemical effects in f-f transitions is quite different from the results of some d-d transitions. In the example of $Fe(CN)_6^{4-}$, all six d electrons are paired into the three t_{2g} orbitals pointing between the ligands. When light puts one of the electrons into an e_g orbital pointing toward the ligands, one of the latter is often expelled and replaced by water. Such d-d absorption thus induces substitution reactions, just as charge-transfer absorption induces redox reactions.

Some of the previously mentioned characteristics of f ions are found, to a smaller degree, in the colors of hydrated d ions. In the very pale violet iron alum, for example, the Fe^{3+} ion has an exactly half-full d subshell. Charge-transfer absorption in the more commonly observed yellowish ions $FeOH^{2+}$ or $FeCl^{2+}$ results from ligands more polarizable than H_2O.

Some other compounds of the same transition elements have extremely intense colors due to a kind of charge-transfer process. The very dark color of $KFe^{II}Fe^{III}(CN)_6$—and of many other substances in mixed oxidation states—arises from the great ease of exchanging electrons between two oxidation states when both are stable and the environmental "furniture" needs very little rearrangement. In contrast, $KCo^{II}Co^{III}(CN)_6$ is pink. In this case the $Co(CN)_6{}^{3-}$ has no low-lying orbital vacancies for acceptance of another electron. This lack of reducibility again correlates with a relative faintness of color.

REFERENCES

1. G. M. Barrow, *Introduction to Molecular Spectroscopy* (New York: McGraw-Hill, 1962), Chapters 10 and 11, "Electronic Spectra. . . ."
2. L. Pauling, *The Nature of the Chemical Bond* (3rd Ed., Ithaca, New York: Cornell, 1960), Section 3–11, "The Correlation of Color and Bond Character."
3. (a) L. E. Orgel, "Charge Transfer Spectra . . . ," *Quart. Rev.* (1954), **8**, 422. (b) Orgel, *An Introduction to Transition-Metal Chemistry* (London: Methuen, 1960), Sections 3.3 and 3.4, on the ease of spin-pairing in octahedral and non-octahedral complexes.
4. C. K. Jørgensen, *Inorganic Complexes* (New York: Academic Press, 1964), emphasis on spectra; earlier books by Jørgensen have similar emphases.
5. *Modern Coordination Chemistry*, eds. J. Lewis and R. G. Wilkins, (New York: Interscience, 1960), T. M. Dunn, Chapter 4, "The Visible and Ultraviolet Spectra of Complex Compounds"; Dunn, "Appraisal of experiment and theory in the spectra of complexes," *Pure Applied Chem.* (1963), **6**, 1.

8

Reactivity in Precipitation
and Complexation

8-1   INTRODUCTION

Formation of a stable soluble complex is not the same as formation of a stable insoluble compound, yet the two are closely related. Thus, corresponding to most precipitates we have complex ions formed with similar bonding from the same or compositionally similar anions. Examples are: AgI and both AgI_2^- and Ag_2I^+; $Fe(CN)_2$ and $Fe(CN)_6^{4-}$; $MgCO_3$ and $Mg(C_2O_4)_2^{2-}$; $AlPO_4$ and $AlP_3O_{10}^{2-}$; iron(III) 8-hydroxyquinolinate and iron(III) 8-hydroxyquinolinate-5-sulfonate ion. It will therefore be convenient to discuss complexes and precipitates together.

In the case of many complex ions, such as the last three mentioned, the ability of the noncoordinated oxygen atoms to hydrogen bond with water must be one important factor against precipitation. Even a hydration free energy of only a little over 1kcal/mole corresponds to a factor of 10 in the equilibrium constant; recall

$$\Delta G \text{ (or } \Delta F) = -RT \ln K = -1.364 \log K \qquad (8\text{--}1)$$

Unfortunately, we do not generally have thermodynamic data on the hydration of complex ions.

This chapter presents and interprets the broad patterns of reactivity, not primarily the smaller differences within series of closely related ligands, except where these expose or confirm a basic principle. Such series are widely studied, in order to isolate one factor, but the student has a prior need for a general background. Moreover, we may often think we have isolated one factor when, in fact, precisely because we are considering closely related substances, several factors are varying in the same manner, but we have recognized only one.

8-2 SALTS WITH MINIMUM POLARIZATION

We begin our study of complex formation and precipitation with cations and anions whose large sizes, small charges, and small tendencies toward polarization or covalent bonding minimize their interactions with each other and with water. K^+ and ClO_4^- are familiar examples and it is well known that they form practically no important complexes or precipitates with other common ions such as OH^- and PO_4^{3-} or Ag^+ and Pb^{2+}, and so on. For this reason it is of interest that the former ions and others like them are precisely the ones that do form, with each other, salts of moderate or low solubility (Table 8–1). In addition to K^+, Rb^+ and Cs^+, a sampling of cations that normally precipitate only anions with a large ratio of size to charge might include

$$As(C_6H_5)_4^+, Co(C_5H_5)_2^+, Ni(NH_3)_6^{2+}, Fe(C_{12}N_2H_8)_3^{2+},$$

$Mn(CO)_6^+$ (probably), $Cu[CS(NH_2)_2]_3^+$, alkaloids, and many others. The large anions show at least as much variety, and are given below in several groups.

The main reason for this phenomenon is probably that, although the electrostatic force between two ions varies inversely as the square of the distance between their centers, the force between a large ion and an idealized dipole (only approximated by water) varies inversely as the cube of the distance if the dipole has a fixed orientation, or as the fifth power of distance if the dipole is free to rotate due to a very large size-to-charge ratio in the ion. The presence of many nonideal dipolar molecules (as in water) complicates and weakens but does not destroy the argument. For such ions, then, hydration energies must be even smaller than the admittedly small interionic energies. Entropy effects may also be important.[1] Solubility in a very different solvent, for example, SO_2, should naturally be affected by the same causes to a different extent, and by others such as Lewis acid character or interaction of π electrons between solvent and solute.

Among the larger cations, NH_4^+ has a mixed behavior. It is similar in size to K^+, but some of its salts, for instance those with ClO_4^-, PF_6^- or BF_4^-, are considerably more soluble. In these cases, the ability of NH_4^+ to hydrogen bond with water must be important. The low solubility of the tetraalkylammonium salts supports this, especially since comparison of the methyl and ethyl substituents shows that size is not the only factor.

Ammonium ion behaves nearly like potassium ion, however, toward other anions such as $C_6H_2(NO_2)_3O^-$ (picrate), $PMo_{12}O_{40}^{3-}$, $IrCl_6^{2-}$, or $HC_4H_4O_6^-$ (acid tartrate). In many of these the negative charge is larger or more localized, presumably promoting hydrogen bonding within the solid. But NH_4^+ $B(C_6H_5)_4^-$ is also very insoluble.

A further need for caution with any simple explanation is brought out by $Ni(NH_3)_6I_2$, whose solubility is very slight. We might have expected that the cation should form hydrogen bonds with water much more than with the anion. The results can be rationalized, but could they have been predicted?

Other anions resembling perchlorate, fluoroborate, and fluorophosphate are $PO_2F_2^-$, SO_3F^-, IO_4^-, MnO_4^-, TcO_4^-, and ReO_4^-; lesser degrees of resemblance are seen in BrO_3^-, IO_3^-, $B(C_6H_5)_4^-$, $Cr(NH_3)_2(NCS)_4^-$, $Re(C_5H_5)_2^-$, $B_{12}H_{12}^{2-}$, I_5^-, $Pt(NO_2)_4^{2-}$, $SiW_{12}O_{40}^{4-}$, and BiI_4^-, which merely illustrate the types that react with various polarizing cations as well as with certain large nonpolarizing ones. These more reactive anions either have larger charges, more polarizable exposed atoms, or multiple bonds; their reactions with the more polarizing cations are essentially covered in Section 8–4. The chemistry of $V(CO)_6^-$ is not well known, but it should precipitate *at least* the cesium-like ions.

$KAsF_6$ and $KSbF_6$ are easily soluble, apparently because of rapid hydrolysis of the anions.

Some anions of intermediate size, for example I^- and Br_3^-, may precipitate the large, complex, nonpolarizing cations but not some or any of the alkali-metal ions. SiF_6^{2-}, on the other hand, forms slightly soluble salts with Ba^{2+} and all the alkali-

Table 8-1 Solubilities of Certain Salts*

	Li^+	Na^+	K^+	Rb^+	Cs^+	NH_4^+	$N(CH_3)_4^+$	$N(C_2H_5)_4^+$
F^-	0.10	1.0	16.	13.	21.	27. (0°)		
IO_3^-	4.4	0.44	0.35	0.081	0.084	0.13		
BF_4^-		9.8	0.035	0.027	0.047	2.4		
ClO_4^-	5.6	17.	0.12	0.71	0.084	2.1	0.065	0.11
IO_4^-		0.48	0.0022	0.023	0.066	0.13		
MnO_4^-	3.9		0.40	0.052	0.009	0.58		
ReO_4^-	1.3	3.5	0.034	0.031	0.020	0.23		
$B(C_6H_5)_4^-$		0.88	0.00018	0.000023	0.000028	0.00029	0.00004	
$AuCl_4^-$	1.8	1.7	1.2	0.27	0.027			
PF_6^-		5.	0.43	0.076	0.030	4.6	0.0077	0.029
$Al(SO_4)_2^-$ aq		4.5	0.24	0.050	0.006	0.33		
SiF_6^{2-}	2.7	0.035	0.006	0.0050	0.015	1.1		
TiF_6^{2-}	1.4	0.31	0.049	0.024	0.059	1.3		
$PtCl_6^{2-}$		1.2	0.03	0.0024	0.0020	0.02		
$Co(NO_2)_6^{3-}$			0.0019	0.000086	0.000068	0.023		

	Be^{2+}	Mg^{2+}	Ca^{2+}	Sr^{2+}	Ba^{2+}	Ra^{2+}
F^-	11.!	0.0027	0.00035	0.00058	0.018	6×10^{-8}
OH^-	1.4×10^{-7}	0.00013	0.021	0.065	0.28	
IO_3^-		0.22	0.0014	0.00060	0.000035	
CO_3^{2-}	0.025 (0°)	0.0063	0.000083	0.000026	0.00004	
SO_3^{2-}		0.06	0.00012	0.00020	0.00003	
SO_4^{2-}	2.4	1.1	0.0049	0.00087	0.000039	
SeO_4^{2-}	2.5	2.1	0.35	0.006	5.3×10^{-6}	
CrO_4^-		8.0	0.026	0.006	9.2×10^{-6}	
$S_2O_3^{2-}$		2.5	4.	0.86	0.0080	
$C_2O_4^{2-}$	2.6	0.0093	0.000036	0.0024	0.00012	
SiF_6^{2-}		2.4		0.12	0.0011	
$Fe(CN)_6^{4-}$		0.70	1.7	0.76	0.0029	

*Molar or *molal* at about 25°.

metal ions except Li^+. Even with the larger, univalent ions, relative solubilities are not determined strictly by size, as brought out by Table 8–1.

Some cases of low solubility might at first appear to be due mainly to the size factor, but further study shows other causes to be important, also. One illustration is $Pt(NH_3)_4PtCl_4$, whose crystal structure and spectra point to Pt—Pt bonding between the parallel cations and anions.

A different case is Tl_2PtCl_6. This has a solubility much lower than that of any alkali-metal chloroplatinate, although Tl^+ and Rb^+ are about the same size, and $TlClO_4$, in addition, is rather *more* soluble (0.5 M) than even $KClO_4$ (0.12 M). These and many other facts, including the insolubility of compounds like Tl_2S, show that Tl^+ has moderate polarizing strength, for example, for chlorine or sulfur atoms or ions (in $PtCl_6^{2-}$ and S^{2-}) or even water molecules (in the perchlorate solution), but not, of course, toward perchlorate ion. This polarizing strength is admittedly less than that of Ag^+ but is the reason for excluding Tl^+ from the list of cesium-type cations above, that do not have such characteristics.

In the interesting quantitative precipitation of

$$[Co(NH_3)_6^{3+}]_2[Th(CO_3)_5^{6-}],$$

we have both large sizes and large charges. Probably internal H bonding is important here. But the anion could also be partly dissociated, even in the solid.

Certain double salts of low solubility may come under the rule concerning large ions of small charge, even though they appear to contain highly charged ions. Examples are the alums, $M^+M^{3+}(XY_4^{2-})_2 \cdot 12H_2O$, and Tutton salts, $(M^+)_2M^{2+}(XY_4^{2-})_2 \cdot 6H_2O$. Here XY_4 may stand for SO_4, SeO_4, or BeF_4.[4] The univalent M is one of the larger alkali-metal ions or ammonium. The bivalent and tervalent M's represent Mg or Al or appropriate transition elements with roughly similar ionic sizes. Independent evidence is still meager, but saturated solutions of these salts must contain considerable concentrations of the outer-sphere complexes $[M(H_2O)_6^{2+, \, 3+}(XY_4^{2-})_2]^{2-, \, -}$. Some of these complexes with sulfate are already known to have dissociation constants around 10^{-3}. (Most bivalent anions excluded here are more basic and expected to favor hydrolysis or inner-sphere complexes more than sulfate does.) The large anions can then form crystals with spaces for one loosely hydrated or two unhydrated, moderately large, univalent cations. Some of the more soluble double salts, such as iron alums, are shown by color changes to undergo rapid transformation in solution from the outer-sphere to a slightly preferred inner-sphere structure with less symmetrical ions. In chromium alums this is slower, and in the aluminum compounds probably less preferred thermodynamically for reasons covered in Section 8–4. In any case, it seems wise here to insert a *caveat*— the species in a solid do not *necessarily* reflect the major species in solution.

A few simple salts of SO_4^{2-}, SeO_4^{2-}, CrO_4^{2-}, and BeF_4^{2-} show the same inverse dependence of solubility on size of cation but different dependences on charge and polarizing strength. A strong downward trend is found in the solubilities of the sulfate-type salts in the series Be^{2+}, Mg^{2+}, Ca^{2+}, Sr^{2+}, Ba^{2+}, and Ra^{2+}, but not in the alkali metal series with the lower cationic charge. Ag^+, Tl^+, Hg_2^{2+}, and Pb^{2+} also form slightly soluble salts, especially with CrO_4^{2-}, but hardly (Pb^{2+}, 0.013 M solubility at 30°) or not at all (otherwise) with BeF_4^{2-}. By now, this should not surprise us; the fluorine atoms are expected to interact much less than the relatively polarizable oxygen atoms (or even the moderately accessible chromium atom) with these highly polarizing and polarizable cations (see Section 8–4).

The anions of the previous paragraph seem to hint at a preference for precipitating cations of the same (absolute) charge, suggesting that in a few cases simple formulas may lead to particularly efficient crystal packing. Perhaps this helps to account for insolubility in a compound like $Co(NH_3)_6Co(CN)_6$, or even in the isoelectronic series $KClO_4$, $CaSO_4$, and $ScPO_4$, because most other combinations of the same ions do not precipitate so easily. In any case, we have probably been fortunate to have considerable success with the principles discussed so far, and below, without reference to the specific crystal structures involved.

8-3 OXY-ANIONS: THE EFFECT OF IONIC ACIDITY AND BASICITY [5a, 6a]

We have seen that the anions most clearly showing the effect of large size and small charge, without complications from polarization, are certain oxy- and fluoro-anions. We now examine the other anions containing these elements from the upper right-hand corner of the periodic table. Table 8–2 is a highly condensed distillation of thousands of possible reactions between oxy-anions and most of the simple cations of the periodic table with the exception of the alkali-metal ions. Reactions with silver and mercury ions (see next section) are also excluded since these highly polarizing ions are practically the only common ones that react with certain anions. This condensed table is possible because most oxy-anions are much less discriminating than sulfide or cyanide, for instance. Mere formation of outer-sphere complexes is not intentionally included. We have also tried to exclude hydrolysis and redox or other irrelevant processes, together with anions dominated by coordination through atoms other than oxygen. Where not much is known of an anion, classification is on what is known. For example, Ba_2XeO_6 is reported to be very insoluble in water and even Na_4XeO_6 dissolves only to the extent of about 0.025 M at ordinary conditions. (The latter result reminds us of the small solubility of sodium salts of antimonate(V) [used as a precipitant for Na^+], tellurate(VI), and iodate(VII) in the same row of the periodic table.) We can therefore expect that many other xenates(VIII) will be insoluble. (See Reference 17 in Chapter 5 for confirmation of this prediction.)

Available data again would not be adequate for a complete thermodynamic treatment of most of the anions considered here. It has been found, however, that the entropy effect is often the main driving force in complex formation between polyvalent cations and oxy-anions.[7a] That is, the joining of the two ions permits a significant disruption of the orderly hydration spheres around them. This is sometimes opposed by the heat effect, because the combining of the ions may release less heat than is absorbed by partly dehydrating them. In the following discussion, quite a different point of view and purpose are adopted and adapted to the information at hand for most of the oxy-anions.

The arrangement in Table 8–2 is according to increasing values of what we might call the "effective basicity" B_{eff} of the anion A^{n-}. This basicity is taken as the negative logarithm of the ratio of activity of the ion to that of the undissociated acid

Table 8-2 Complexing and Precipitation of Oxy-Anions

Anion	B_{eff}	B_{adj}	Comments
ClO_4^-	−5.6		negligible
*ClO_3^-	−1.0		negligible
$S_2O_8^{2-}$			negligible
MnO_4^-	−0.5		negligible
HSO_4^-	−0.3		negligible
NO_3^-	0.4	−5.3	negligible
ReO_4^-	0.5		negligible
*BrO_3^-	1.1		few sl sol
$CF_3CO_2^-$	1.5		negligible
*$CCl_3CO_2^-$	1.9		negligible
*$C_6H_2(NO_2)_3O^-$	2.1	4.1	few sl sol
*IO_3^-	2.5		many sl sol
*$SO_3NH_2^-$	2.7		negligible
$PH_2O_2^-$	2.8		few cpx, ppt
SO_4^{2-}	3.7		several ppt
*ClO_2^-	3.7		negligible
SeO_4^{2-}	3.8		several ppt
$Cr_2O_7^{2-}$	3.8		few ppt
$H_2PO_4^-$	3.9		few sl sol
*$C_6H_5SO_3^-$	4.3		no ppt reported
$P_3O_9^{3-}$			some ppt, cpx
*NO_2^-	5.0		few weak cpx
CHO_2^-	5.5		few ppt, cpx
$CH_3CHOHCO_2^-$	5.6		moderate cpx
HCO_3^-	5.6		few sl sol
$H_2VO_4^-$	5.7	8.2	*most ppt $(VO_3^-)_x$*
*$C_6H_5CO_2^-$	5.9		many sl sol
$CH_3CO_2^-$	6.5	5.3	weak cpx, few ppt
$C_{17}H_{35}CO_2^-$	6.7	9.6	all ppt
$S_2O_6^{2-}$	7.1		no ppt reported
PO_3F^{2-}	8.8	9.	several ppt
$C_2O_4^{2-}$	9.2		all ppt or cpx
*ClO^-	9.3		no ppt reported
MoO_4^{2-}	9.4	11.	most ppt
WO_4^{2-}	9.5	>12.	most ppt
CrO_4^{2-}	10.7	<10.	many ppt
$(CHOHCO_2^-)_2$	10.7		all ppt or cpx
$B(OH)_4^-$	*11.0*		*most ppt $(BO_2^-)_x$*
*$As(OH)_4^-$	11.1		most ppt
PHO_3^{2-}	12.2		most ppt
*SO_3^{2-}	12.5		most ppt or cpx
HPO_4^{2-}	12.8		many ppt
$H_3IO_6^{2-}$	13.5		many ppt or cpx
*TeO_3^{2-}	13.8		most ppt
*SeO_3^{2-}	14.4	15.7	most ppt
OH^-	17.5		most ppt
CO_3^{2-}	17.6		most ppt
*$N_2O_2^{2-}$	21.5		most ppt
$H_4TeO_6^{2-}$	21.5	22.	most ppt or cpx
AsO_3^{3-}	26.0		most ppt
$P_2O_7^{4-}$	26.7		all ppt or cpx
PO_4^{3-}	26.9		all ppt
$P_3O_{10}^{5-}$	27.		all cpx or ppt
XeO_6^{4-}	~40.		all ppt (prediction)

*See textual comments.

(see Equation 8–2) in a hypothetical solution with properties similar to water but with the activity of H_3O^+ or H^+ equal to its value at a mole fraction of 1, or 55.5 M, assuming the ideal behavior thus implied.[8] Thus,

$$B_{\text{eff}} \equiv - \log \frac{[A^{n-}]}{[H_nA]} \equiv \log\left[\frac{[H_nA]}{[H^+]^n[A^{n-}]}[H^+]^n\right] = \Sigma\, pK_{\text{acid}} + 1.74n$$

(8–2)

where activities rather than concentrations are implied by the brackets.

In this definition all the pK's for the acid ionization are used, rather than just the first, because metal ions, at least in precipitates, must neutralize all the negative charges. It is therefore felt that the combined ability to hold hydrogen ions in the acid should be related to the ability to hold metal ions. For considering complex ions separately, we would take only the pK's for the coordinating atoms. In the minority of cases where this makes a difference, it would mean omitting the smallest pK's, representing the first steps of acid ionization or the last steps of association with H^+. The precipitation behavior of most inorganic anions, however, still seems to be better known than their complexing propensities.

The term $1.74n$ is included because a mole fraction of 1 is less arbitrary than 1 mole/liter and because this choice gives a slightly sharper separation of reactive from unreactive ions in a table, such as Table 8–2, whose members have various valences.

The table also includes, where possible, values of what we will call the "adjusted basicity"

$$B_{\text{adj}} \equiv B_{\text{eff}} - \log[H_nA]_{\text{sat}} \equiv - \log[A^{n-}]$$

(8–3)

in a hypothetical solution similar to the above but saturated with the free acid (see Equation 8–3). The term for the solubility of the acid is included because it should and does correlate with solubility of the salts. For example, solubilities generally decrease from acetates to benzoates to stearates, from phosphates to pyrophosphates to triphosphates, and from chromates to molybdates to tungstates, both for the metal salts and for the hydrogen "salts" (acids), even though the effective basicities within each of these sets of anions are fairly constant. In all of these sets the solubility changes are probably related mainly to the greater London (polarization) forces associated with the larger and/or heavier anions. Where H_nA is miscible with or very soluble in water, we use Equation 8–4

$$- \log[H_nA]_{sat} \equiv - \log \text{solubility} = \Delta G/2.3\,RT \qquad (8\text{–}4)$$

together with the free energies of the pure acid and the dissolved acid (both unionized) at unit activity. (For H_2O itself this "solubility" is 55.5 M.) Unfortunately, these free energies are seldom both available.

If the inclusion of this solubility information in these qualitative attempts to predict solubilities seems to be circular reasoning, we can remark that this correction is small, but certainly more importantly, that it is always valuable to be able to predict properties for a large number of combinations (for example, of ions in salts) from the separate properties of a much smaller number of components.

We can now state explicitly, with reference to Table 8–2, what has so far been only partly implied: Oxy-anions having B_{eff} greater than approximately 4 to 6 are generally good complexers and/or precipitants, although values of B_{adj}, where known to be above approximately 6, are probably better indicators of precipitating ability.

Let us now turn to some individual examples. Bromate, iodate, and picrate form less soluble salts with some of the heavier cations, for instance, the ions of barium, thorium, or lead. This may be partly an effect of size as well as of London forces. Numerous others, for example, sulfamate, acid anions, or monocarboxylates, which are singly charged and at least as large as perchlorate do not show this effect, probably because of hydrogen bonding (to solvent) and localization of charge.

The ions marked with asterisks have the possibility of coordinating through atoms more polarizable than oxygen or through π electrons on carbon (as in the well-known benzene-silver ion complex). All of these except sulfamate also have available d orbitals or antibonding molecular orbitals which can receive back-donated electrons. Most of these have compounds of silver and mercury, at least, which are much less soluble than their other compounds and which are sometimes just about the only insoluble ones. Even hypochlorite, not reported to yield any precipitates or complexes, rapidly disproportionates in the presence of silver ion; this suggests at least a temporary complex. All of these anions could perhaps be considered in the next section, but polarizable atoms such as sulfur show their characteristic effects most clearly only in negative oxidation states as, for example, in $S_2O_3^{2-}$, whose type of anion therefore does come later. (Nevertheless, thiosulfate resembles sulfate, not too surprisingly, in precipitating barium ion.)

All of the d-element anions also seem to have special affinities for heavy metal cations such as those of silver and mercury.

The precipitation of *normal* carbonates, sulfates, and phosphates from HCO_3^-, HSO_4^-, $H_2PO_4^-$, and HPO_4^{2-} are not counted for the latter acid anions. On the other hand, precipitations of *polymerized* borates and vanadates are included in Table 8–2, mainly because "normal" precipitates (especially orthoborates) are less known.

The basicities calculated make no allowance for the chelate effect in ions such as lactate or tartrate, whose hydroxyl groups do not easily ionize, but still help to stabilize complexes. In strongly basic solution they may ionize and they do strongly complex most cations but then, correspondingly, the appropriate basicities would also be much larger if known.

8-4   OTHER LIGANDS: EFFECTS RELATED TO POLARIZATION AND COVALENCY

The chemistries of fluoride and iodide ions present a striking contrast, in fact, almost a paradox. The ions are of the same family, they have the same charge, and both are monatomic; neither is strongly basic. Yet fluorides and fluoro-complexes of calcium, aluminum, zirconium, etc. are familiar in nature and in the analytical laboratory, while those of mercury and related cations are curiosities; with iodides this is precisely reversed.

The ability of fluoride ion to precipitate or coordinate cations having the inert-gas structure does correlate broadly with their acidity or charge and size. Even the alkali-metal ions show the affinity of fluoride for small cations (Table 8–1). But the dominance of different factors is equally clear in the reactions of iodide, sulfide, or other polarizable oxidizable anions of low-electronegativity elements. Aluminum sulfide, for instance, is much less stable (toward water) than silver iodide, in spite of the fact that the acidity and basicity, the small sizes, and the large charges of the ions all favor the former.

Figure 8–1, due to A. F. Clifford, shows that the solubility

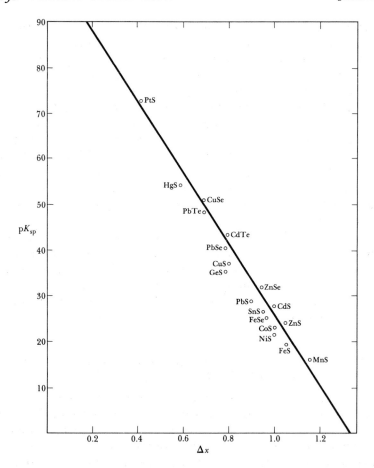

Fig. 8–1. Solubility products of MS, MSe, and MTe versus differences in Pauling electronegativities.

products of bivalent sulfides, selenides, and tellurides correlate well with the (Pauling) electronegativity difference. Therefore, the stability, as measured by solubility product, depends here on the degree of covalency, as measured by electronegativity difference. Let us not forget, however, that stability of a species is not absolute, but is relative to the reaction being considered. A mainly covalent bond will obviously resist dissociation into *ions*, but not necessarily into the neutral elements. In the latter respect, an ionic bond is more stable, as we already know. Figure

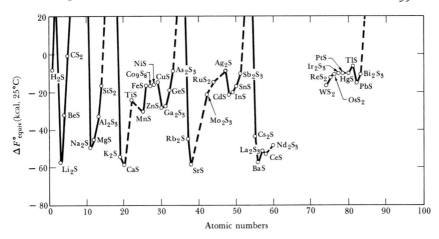

Fig. 8–2. Equivalent standard free energies of formation of sulfides.

8–2, due to J. A. Allen, brings this out, even for sulfides, by comparing the standard free energies of formation from the elements.

It would be surprising if the stabilities of fluorides and salts of oxy-acids depended only on basicity of anion and acidity of cation while combinations with other ligands were affected only by electronegativity or related parameters.[9-10] It is more reasonable to assume that both factors, and others, will enter to different extents in all cases. A hint of the complexity of the other factors is given by Fig. 8–3 (adapted from Reference 24, following S. Ahrland *et al.*), showing the average coordination number, $\bar{n}$, of ligand groups attached to just one kind of cation, *i.e.,* Ag^+, at various concentrations of ligand ($pL \equiv -\log$ [ligand]). Here we see distinct tendencies toward the coordination numbers 1, 2, 3, or 4, arising from influences such as charge, polarity, polarizability, size, or back-donation of metal electrons, and still excluding chelation or changes of medium or temperature. Nevertheless, the more strongly bonded groups are the more polarizable ones.

In order to handle the larger trends associated with two or three dominant factors, we refer to the concept of linear free-energy relations, as discussed by Edwards and, in other terms, by others.[11] Free-energy changes (including those for activated states) are proportional to logarithms of equilibrium or rate constants. Therefore correlations of rates of substitution reac-

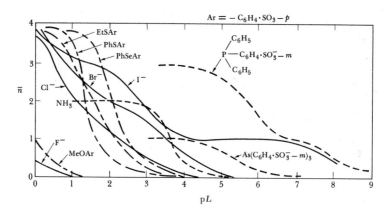

Fig. 8–3. Average coordination number of Ag+ versus – log[ligand].

tions, for example, have been made using equations of the form

$$\log k = aA + bB + c \qquad (8–5)$$

where A and B represent, for one reagent, parameters that can sometimes be determined independently of the reaction in question, whereas a, b, and c are adjusted to the other reagent and the type of reaction. It now seems desirable to look for equations of the form

$$\log K = m(AB + XY + \ldots) + n \qquad (8–6)$$

where m and n depend only on the type of reaction, and A and X, as well as B and Y, can be evaluated independently for both the electrophilic and nucleophilic reagents, respectively.

For our present purposes, A and B might stand for some appropriate measure of acidity of the cation and basicity of the ligand, or perhaps for the purely electrostatic effects. X and Y, in compatible units, could be functions of either electronegativity or parameters of localized polarization or one-electron redox capability, because all of these relate to the strength of covalent bonding. (The importance of localized properties is illustrated by NCS⁻, which attaches by the more polarizable S to the heavier cations, otherwise by the smaller N atom.) Also related in some degree would be Jørgensen's nephelauxetic series in spectroscopy,[12] the trans-effect series in inorganic substitutions, orientation and activation series in aromatic substitutions, and so on. All of these can be criticized, but here we will use the former concepts qualitatively to help explain the main trends in reactivity.

Let us now return to specific examples. We mentioned that fluoride ion (which has a moderate basicity but less polarizability than any other ligand) reacts with noble-gas type cations best if they are small, highly charged, and acidic. Thus, one analytical procedure calls for dissolving calcium fluoride by use of aluminum ion, which has a large affinity for fluoride ion. On the other hand, Hg^{2+} is both smaller and more acidic than Pb^{2+} in the same region of the periodic table, yet the first ion is unreactive to F^-, except for the indirect effect of hydrolysis caused by the basicity of fluoride, while the second precipitates PbF_2. We might at first suppose that, if the various effects add up, as suggested by the linear free-energy concept, and even if the great polarizing strength of mercury(II) has no effect on fluoride ion, the mercury compound would still have to be the more stable one.

We must, therefore, consider the profound influence of the solvent. In Fig. 5-1 we saw that water is held inordinately strongly by the most highly polarizing heavy-metal cations. These cations therefore prefer coordination with H_2O or OH^-, whose oxygen atom is more polarizable and less electronegative than fluorine, to coordination with F^-. In an additive free-energy relation, all this could be expressed, even without explicit attention to the solvent, simply by defining the parameter Y in Equation 8-6 so as to have a negative value in the case of fluoride ion.

Many of our discussions have involved mercury or silver ions. There are others of the same type, of course, but not many, and they do not occur in appreciable concentrations as simple aquated ions (or stable fluoro-complexes). Pt^{4+} is one example that *is* known in a fluoride complex, *i.e.*, PtF_6^{2-}, but this has the expected instability in water. As also expected from their other properties, most d-element cations have intermediate characteristics in formation of precipitates and complexes. The small differences among many of these cations can be explained both by trends in electronegativity and polarization, as discussed here, and also largely by ligand-field effects; the latter, however, do not apply to the whole periodic table.

The same dependence of stability on polarization appears in various more exotic cases which often seem surprising without this understanding. Thus the exceedingly reduction-stable $CoCpd_2^+$ precipitates large anions including ClO_4^-, $Co(CO)_4^-$, $PtCl_6^{2-}$, $Cr(NH_3)_2(NCS)_4^-$, $B(C_6H_5)_4^-$, $C_6H_2(NO_2)_3O^-$, Br_3^-, I_3^-, BiI_4^-, HgI_4^{2-}, and even NO_3^-, but it forms very soluble compounds with highly hydrated F^-, OH^-, CN^-, CO_3^{2-}, and PO_4^{3-}. All of this is about as expected for a large, inert, univalent cation. The similar cation $FeCpd_2^+$ also precipitates such oxidizable or polarizable large ions as I_3^-, $B(C_6H_5)_4^-$, $Cr(NH_3)_2(NCS)_4^-$, $C_6H_2(NO_2)_3O^-$, and $SiW_{12}O_{40}^{4-}$, but *not* the more oxidation-inert NO_3^- or ClO_4^-. Since ferricenium ion is quite easy to reduce to ferrocene (due to a single low-lying electron vacancy) it should be a fairly good polarizer and therefore should and does bond to the less inert water molecules rather than to nitrate or perchlorate ions.

The benzene complexes $Cr(C_6H_6)_2^+$ and $Ru(C_6H_6)_2^{2+}$ likewise precipitate various large anions, including at least ClO_4^- and PF_6^-, respectively. This behavior could be due to better shielding of the metal atoms from water molecules by the benzene group, which is larger than the cyclopentadienyl group. It may also arise from a smaller reducibility (compared to $FeCpd_2^+$) of the cations.

A different behavior is found in the borohydride anions. Many of these, of course, are such powerful reducing agents that salts with Ag^+, and so on, cannot even exist. In contrast, $B_{10}H_{10}^{2-}$ and $B_{12}H_{12}^{2-}$ are extremely stable (for borohydrides) but the structure of their molecular orbitals gives them chemical properties like those of aromatic hydrocarbons.[13] This implies considerable polarizability or oxidizability (compared to perchlorate) and essentially explains their precipitation with Cu^+ and Ag^+.[14] (They also precipitate some large, inert cations.) In this connection we may also recall the silver ion–benzene complex and the precipitates of picrate ion with the reducible cations.

With oxy-anions, basicity is the most important factor, as already seen. This is essentially because, compared to the wide range of "polarizabilities" (Y in Equation 8–6) from fluoride to sulfide or iodide, various oxy-anions must have values of Y similar to that of water (possibly defined as zero), with which they must compete for the cations. For complex anions these values cannot yet be measured independently, because they should refer primarily to the atom actually coordinated to the metal and should not include the effect of negative charge already accounted for by basicity. The basicities represent partly a longer range force and vary more with charge and size. In fact, it is desirable to have a kind of "basicity" depending only on electrostatic interactions including dipole effects. After all, basicity as defined by reactivity with hydrogen ion is defined by a fairly reducible and electronegative ion. Something like aluminum ion might be a "purer" standard for an empirical definition. Z/r^2, like the ionic potential[15] Z/r, is attractive as a more independent definition but is not applicable to many complex ions. Likewise, fluoride ion would provide a better test of "acidity" than would hydroxide ion. Unfortunately, we still do not have enough data to set up fairly complete tables based on quantitative definitions of these types.

Sulfide ion is both basic and polarizable and therefore reacts with a wide variety of cations. However, combinations with acidic cations of only normal polarizing strength such as Al^{3+} often result mostly in hydrolysis. (An interesting exception is BeS, reported to be insoluble in water.) This is consistent with the fact that H^+ is fairly electronegative as well as acidic and is a better partner than aluminum ion for sulfide ion. OH^- is likewise more basic than S^{2-} and so has the greater affinity for Al^{3+}.

Ligands coordinating through the nonmetals in periodic columns **p2** and **p3**, namely, cyanide, amines, phosphines, and so on, are not treated with complete success, even qualitatively, by Equation 8–6 as it stands. The basic ligands prefer hydrolysis to reaction with ions of the aluminum type and presumably for the same reason as above. But the reactions with **p** cations (for example, Pb^{2+}) are also weak, while reactions with late **d** cations (for example, Pd^{2+}) are much enhanced, particularly with cyanide.

On probing a little deeper, however, we find that, even with a late **d** cation like Pt^{4+}, the bond strengths of the halide complexes are in the perhaps surprising order

$$F^- > Cl^- > Br^- > I^-,$$

but the countervailing hydration energies of the anions are in the same order and with larger differences.[16] This order, in both cases, is expected even for purely electrostatic interactions with anions of increasing size. In addition, such highly reducible cations, as assumed before, do have greater *covalent* bonding with the most oxidizable anions, and this partly equalizes the total bonding to the metal, leaving the balance of power with the hydration energies. Or, as is more convenient here, we may say that the trends in the electrostatic factors roughly cancel each other, giving the decision to the covalent forces.

The back-donation of electrons from transitional atoms, especially in zero and negative oxidation states, to unsaturated ligands such as cyanide (as in $Ag(CN)_2^-$) is now widely recognized. This means that we need a term in Equation 8–6 representing the product of the (π electron) oxidizability or polarizability of the *cation* and the reducibility or *corresponding* polarizing strength of the *anion*. With this addition the behavior of the carbon-coordinating ligands is qualitatively accounted for. At the same time the difficulties of a complete quantitative treatment are increased, although appropriate parameters such as orbital electronegativities may follow from the work of Hinze and Jaffé (Section 3–2). The back-donation may occur to some extent with ions like sulfide and iodide, but not with saturated amines.

The increment of stability with nonchelated **d** ion ammines (say, $Cu(NH_3)_4^{2+}$) is not so large, and an effect has been observed which may account for at least some of it.[17] To explain infrared results, it is suggested that there is a kind of internal hydrogen bonding involving the same metal electrons that would be donated to cyanide (see Fig. 8–4). Substituted, especially tertiary, amines should have less of this influence, and they are in fact weaker coordinating agents to metal ions in spite of being more basic to H^+. This is so even in the first stage of coordination and with $Ag(N[CH_3]_3)_2^+$, where steric hindrance, except to H_2O, cannot be involved. Alternative explanations have invoked steric exclusion of water, in the substituted amines, or enhancement of amine-to-water hydrogen bonding by cation-induced polarization, in the unsubstituted ones.[18-20]

The surprisingly sharp drop, between **d10** and **p1** elements, in the ability to coordinate nitrogen and carbon, has been used in an analytical scheme[21] based on precipitation of uni- and bivalent transition cations by $Co(CN)_6^{3-}$. But the isoelectronic $Fe(CN)_6^{4-}$, which is more basic and highly charged, precipitates most of the common cations.

A further interesting manifestation of back-donation is probably seen in BH_3CO and compounds of higher boron hy-

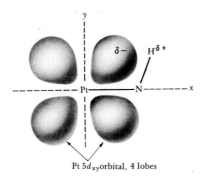

Fig. 8-4.   Internal H bonding between the N—H of an amine and a metal *d* orbital.

drides with some of the ligands that complex transition elements. Thus, boron hydrides, being electron deficient, can accept ligand electrons and, being composed of electropositive elements with some electrons having appropriate symmetries, can also donate electrons (by hyperconjugation) back into ligand π orbitals. The combination of these properties causes a certain resemblance to the transition metals, as well as to the aromatic hydrocarbons.

8-5   SOME REGULARITIES AMONG THE CATIONS

Differences among the simple metal cations are considerably less than those among the common anions and neutral ligands, which may be simple or complex, singly or multiply bonded, or of various shapes. Considerable attention has been given, however, to orders of stability for complexes of oxy-anions and nitrogen-coordinating ligands with bivalent cations, especially the late **3d** series.[5c, 6b, 20b, 22-25] Here, it is usually found that stabilities of high-spin complexes are in the order:

$$Cr^{2+} > Mn^{2+} < Fe^{2+} < Co^{2+} < Ni^{2+} < Cu^{2+} > Zn^{2+}.$$

This also appears to be the order of toxicities, acidities, electron affinities and, approximately, of ligand-field effects. Differences of coordination number and geometry complicate the interpretations, but it is reasonable to assign acidity of cations a role corresponding to that of basicity of oxy-anions in complexes between the two.

Frequently, the ions of lead, the alkaline earths, and heavy **d** elements are placed in the same one-dimensional series although their positions are less fixed and this procedure confuses the evidence for periodicity. However, we can certainly write $Ca^{2+} < Mn^{2+} < Zn^{2+}$ for the configurations $3d^0$, $3d^5$ and $3d^{10}$ with no ligand-field effects. We also often find

$$Mg^{2+} > Ca^{2+} > Sr^{2+} > Ba^{2+},$$

correlating with size or acidity, but frequently

$$Mg^{2+} < Ca^{2+} > Sr^{2+} > Ba^{2+}.$$

The smallest cation must still have the greatest attraction for the ligands, but the hold on water molecules, we recall, is also great, and the balance is rather delicate.

We have already considered, in the previous section, some of the distinctions between the more reducible and less reducible ("soft" and "hard"[26]) cations in their reactions with polarizable ("soft") ligands. It should now be pointed out that some of the differences among the reducible cations are partly due to differences in hydration. For example, Cu^{2+} and Hg^{2+} have comparable excess polarizing strengths (Table 4–3), but numerous mercuric complexes are much more stable than the corresponding cupric ones. The mercuric ion, however, is the larger one and so is considerably less hydrated (Fig. 5–1). A detailed consideration of these points, to which space cannot be given here, should lead to the conclusion that these results are qualitatively as expected on the basis of the principles presented earlier. As discussed elsewhere,[7a] though, the comparisons are based on the ionization energies. This will exaggerate the effect of hydration by assigning all the influence of size to hydration energy, but none to ionization energy (as corrected, however, in Table 4–3).

To summarize the broad patterns of complexation and precipitation, excluding **s** element ions, a mnemonic idea may sometimes be useful: the heavier metal atoms and ions unite best with ligands that expose the heavier nonmetal atoms in a given family; similarly, the lighter members of each group tend, in comparison, to unite with the lighter members of the other. In addition, ligands (such as CN^- and NH_3) containing elements from the left side of the nonmetal region in the periodic table normally combine with metal species (that is, those in the **d** groups) toward the left. The halogens, toward the right, are less discriminating but often found with **p** cations and late **d** cations (likewise toward the right side) in stable combinations.

REFERENCES

1. R. M. Diamond, "The Aqueous Solution Behavior of Large Univalent Ions. A New Type of Ion-Pairing," *J. Phys. Chem.* (1963), **67**, 2513, revealing important entropy effects.

2. H. S. Booth and D. R. Martin, *Boron Trifluoride and Its Derivatives* (New York: Wiley, 1949), Chapter 5, "Fluoboric Acids and Their Salts."

3. *Fluorine Chemistry*, ed. J. H. Simons (New York: Academic, 1950): **I**, W. Lange, Chapter 3, "The Chemistry of the Fluoro Acids of Fourth, Fifth and Sixth Group Elements"; *ibid.* (1954), **II**, A. G. Sharpe, Chapter 1, "Fluorine Containing Complex Salts and Acids." Also, *Adv. Fluorine Chem.*, eds. M. Stacey, J. C. Tatlow, and A. G. Sharpe (London: Butterworths, 1960), **1**, 68, "Fluoboric Acids."

4. A. K. Ghosh and N. N. Ray, *Z. anorg. allgem. Chem.* (1959), **300**, 102, and earlier on fluoroberyllates.

5. (a) A. E. Martell and M. Calvin, *Chemistry of the Metal Chelate Compounds* (Englewood Cliffs, New Jersey: Prentice-Hall, 1952), Section 4.4, "Basic Strength and Chelate Stability." (b) *Ibid.*, Section 4.6, "Nature of the Donor Atom." (c) *Ibid.*, Chapter 5, "Effect of Metal Ion"; also S. Chaberek and Martell, *Organic Sequestering Agents* (New York: Wiley, 1959), Section 4.16, briefer but more recent.

6. (a) *The Chemistry of the Coordination Compounds*, ed. J. C. Bailar, Jr. (New York: Reinhold, 1956), R. W. Parry and R. N. Keller, pp. 177–183, "Stability of Complexes . . . The Role of the Ligand"; also pp. 139–142. (b) *Ibid.*, Keller and Parry, pp. 174–177, ". . . The Role of the Metal."

7. (a) R. J. P. Williams, "The Stability of Complex Ions with Special Reference to Hydration," *J. Phys. Chem.* (1954), **58**, 121. (b) Williams, "The Complexes of B-Sub-group Metals," *Proc. Chem. Soc.* (1960), 20. See also Williams, "A Systematic . . . Choice of Organic Reagents for Metal Ions," *Analyst* (1953), **78**, 586.

8. R. W. Gurney, *Ionic Processes in Solution* (New York: McGraw-Hill, 1953), pp. 88–91, on correcting to a mole fraction of 1.

9. L. G. Van Uitert and W. C. Fernelius, *J. Am. Chem. Soc.* (1954), **76**, p. 375 (abstract)—nitrogen chelates "show a greater dependency upon metal ion electronegativity than those bonding through oxygen"; *ibid.*, p. 379, on the correlation of stabilities of N and O chelates with a product of electronegativities, etc.

10. S. Ahrland, J. Chatt, and N. R. Davies, "Relative Affinities of Ligand Atoms for Acceptor Molecules and Ions," *Quart. Rev.* (1958), **12**, 265.

11. J. O. Edwards, *Mechanisms of Inorganic Reactions* (New York: Benjamin, 1964), Sections 3–1 to 3–5 on "Linear Free-Energy Relations" and Sections 4–2 to 4–7 on applications to kinetics. See also: *J. Am. Chem. Soc.* (1954), **76**, 1540; (1956), **78**, 1819; (1962), **84**, 16. W. P. Jencks and J. Carriuolo, *J. Am. Chem. Soc.* (1960), **82**, 1778, on various factors in the "Reactivity of Nucleophilic Reagents toward Esters." J. F. Bunnett, "Nucleophilic Reactivity," *Ann. Rev. Phys. Chem.* (1963), **14**, 271.

12. C. K. Jørgensen, "The Nephelauxetic Series," *Prog. Inorg. Chem.* (New York: Interscience, 1962), **4**, 73.

13. Anon., *Chem. Eng. News* (January 27, 1964), **42**, 45, on the aromaticity of polyboranes. And see W. H. Knoth *et al.*, *J. Am. Chem. Soc.* (1962), **84**, 1056.

14. W. N. Lipscomb, *Boron Hydrides* (New York: Benjamin, 1963), p. 192 and other sources.

15. G. H. Cartledge, *J. Am. Chem. Soc.* (1928), **50**, 2855 and 2863; *ibid.* (1930), **52**, 3076; Cartledge, *J. Phys. Col. Chem.* (1951), **55**, 248—all on the ionic potential and periodicity, confined to ions of noble-gas structure.

16. A. J. Poë and M. S. Vaidya, "The Relative Stabilities of Halogeno-complexes . . . Bond Strengths," *J. Chem. Soc.* (1961), p. 1023.

17. J. Chatt, L. A. Duncanson, and L. M. Venanzi, "Infra-red spectroscopic evidence of an interaction between the NH bonds of co-ordinated amines and the non-bonding *d*-electrons of metal atoms," *J. Inorg. Nuc. Chem.* (1958), **8**, 67.

18. A. F. Trotman-Dickenson, "The Basic Strength of Amines," *J. Chem. Soc.* (1949), p. 1293, also on stabilities of silver-amine complexes and their enhanced hydrogen-bonding to water.

19. H. Irving and J. M. M. Griffiths, ". . . Complexes . . . with N-Alkyl-substituted Ethylenediamines," *J. Chem. Soc.* (1954), p. 213, including destabilization by steric shielding from water.

20. (a) *Modern Coordination Chemistry,* eds. J. Lewis and R. G. Wilkins (New York: Interscience, 1960), F. J. C. Rossotti, Chapter 1, Section IV, "The Ratio of Successive Stability Constants" and the relation to changing coordination number, etc. (b) *Ibid.,* Section V, "Correlations with Properties of the Metal Ion." (c) *Ibid.,* Section VI, "Correlations with Properties of the Ligand." Also, H. Irving and H. Rossotti, "Some Relationships among the Stabilities of Metal Complexes," *Acta Chem. Scand.* (1956), **10,** 72.

21. R. L. Rich, "The Cyanocobaltate Scheme of Qualitative Analysis," *J. Chem. Ed.* (1962), **39,** 403, in which group separations follow divisions of the periodic table.

22. J. Bjerrum, "On the Tendency of the Metal Ions toward Complex Formation," *Chem. Rev.* (1950), **46,** 381; *ibid.,* 393, on size and charge versus electronegativity.

23. H. Irving and R. J. P. Williams, "The Stability of Transition-metal Complexes," *J. Chem. Soc.* (1953), 3192.

24. *International Conference on Coordination Chemistry, Spec. Pub. 13* (London: The Chemical Society, 1959), H. M. N. H. Irving, p. 13, "The Stability of Metal Complexes," and Fig. 11, classification as (a) or (b) types of "Acceptor atoms in their usual valency states."

25. G. Schwarzenbach, "The General, Selective, and Specific Formation of Complexes by Metallic Cations," *Adv. Inorg. Radiochem.* (New York: Academic Press, 1961), **3,** 257, Sections VI, VII, and VIII: "A- and B-Metal Cations," "Electrovalent and Nonelectrovalent Interaction," and "Transition Metal Cations."

26. R. G. Pearson, "Hard and Soft Acids and Bases," *J. Am. Chem. Soc.* (1963), **85,** 3533; C. K. Jørgensen, " 'Symbiotic' Ligands, Hard and Soft Central Atoms," *Inorg. Chem.* (1964), **3,** 1201; F. Basolo *et al.,* ". . . Steric Factors in . . . M—SCN or M—NCS . . . ," *Inorg. Chem.* (1964), **3,** 1202.

27. G. H. Nancollas, "Thermodynamics of Ion Association in Aqueous Solution," *Quart. Rev.* (1960), **14,** 402.

28. S. Ahrland *et al., Acta Chem. Scand.* (1963), **17,** 1567, includes the effect of oxidation state on π-bonding character.

29. D. M. Gruen and R. McBeth, "The coordination chemistry of 3d transition metal ions in fused salt solutions," *Pure Applied Chem.* (1963), **6,** 23.

30. J. Bjerrum, G. Schwarzenbach, and L. G. Sillén, *Stability Constants, Organic Ligands* and *Inorganic Ligands, Spec. Pub. 6* and *7,* respectively (London: The Chemical Society, 1957 and 1958).

31. K. B. Yatsimirskii and V. P. Vasil'ev, *Instability Constants of Complex Compounds* (New York: Consultants Bureau, 1960).

32. A. D. Gelman, A. I. Moskvin, L. M. Zaitsev, and M. P. Mefod'eva, trans. C. N. Turton and T. I. Turton, *Complex Compounds of Transuranium Elements* (New York: Consultants Bureau, 1962).

33. *Solubility Constants of Metal Oxides, Metal Hydroxides, and Metal Hydroxide Salts in Aqueous Solution,* eds. W. Feitknecht and P. Schindler (London: Butterworths, 1963).

34. H. Taube, *Chem. Rev.* (1952), **50**, 69, on dependence of periodicity in substitution kinetics on electron structure.

35. M. Eigen, *Pure Applied Chem.* (1963), **6**, 97, partly on periodicity of rates in very fast ligand substitutions.

36. M. M. Jones, *Elementary Coordination Chemistry* (Englewood Cliffs, New Jersey: Prentice-Hall, 1964), Chapter IV, "Typical Complexes of the Various Elements," also pp. 40–47.

37. R. M. Diamond, K. Street, Jr., and G. T. Seaborg, "An Ion-exchange Study of Possible Hybridized 5f Bonding in the Actinides," *J. Am. Chem. Soc.* (1954), **76**, 1461.

38. I. Grenthe, "Thermodynamic Properties of Rare Earth Complexes . . . Factors of Importance . . . in Aqueous Solution," *Acta Chem. Scand.* (1964), **18**, 293.

39. T. Moeller *et al.,* "The Coordination Chemistry of Yttrium and the Rare Earth Metal Ions," *Chem. Rev.* (1965), **65.**

40. E. A. Magnusson, *Rev. Pure Appl. Chem.* (1957), **7**, 195, on factors affecting bonding in complexes.

Index